Cory Helps Kids Cope with
Divorce
Playful Therapeutic Activities for Young Children

Liana Lowenstein

Champion Press
Toronto

Library and Archives Canada Cataloguing in Publication

Lowenstein, Liana, 1965-, author
    Cory helps kids cope with divorce : playful therapeutic activities for young children / Liana Lowenstein.

ISBN 978-0-9685199-8-1 (pbk.)

1. Children of divorced parents--Counseling of. 2. Child psychotherapy. 3. Play therapy. I. Title.

HQ777.5.L67 2013   618.92'89142   C2013-905679-3

Correspondence regarding this book can be sent to:
Champion Press
PO Box 91012, 2901 Bayview Avenue, Toronto, Ontario, Canada M2K 2Y6
Telephone: (416) 575-7836
Web: www.lianalowenstein.com

Contents

Acknowledgments

My heartfelt thanks are due first to the children and parents I have worked with over the years, for the many lessons they have taught me. They are the true inspiration for this book.

I owe a tremendous debt of gratitude to Helen Radovanovic, Laurie Stein, Sueann Kenney-Noziska, and Pam Dyson, who so generously donated their time to review my manuscript, providing me with valuable suggestions and encouragement. I am grateful to the colleagues who graciously took the time to try the activities with their clients, and who offered helpful feedback. I also thank Gary Yorke and Deanne Ginns-Gruenberg for their guidance and support. Thanks also to Beth McAuley for her editorial assistance, and to Kim Bracic for her design work.

Special gratitude is expressed to my family and friends for their continued support and encouragement. I am particularly thankful to my husband Steven, for his love and understanding, and to my daughter Jaime, for the joy she brings to my life.

About the Author

Liana Lowenstein, MSW, RSW, CPT-S, is an author, sought-after speaker, and practitioner who has worked with children and their families since 1988. She completed her Master of Social Work degree at the University of Toronto, and she is a Certified Child and Play Therapist (Supervisor) with the Canadian Association for Child and Play Therapy. She provides clinical supervision to mental health practitioners, runs a play-therapy internship program, and consults to several mental health agencies. She has a reputation as a dynamic workshop leader and has presented trainings across North America and abroad. She is the founder of Champion Press Publishing Company and has authored numerous publications, including the highly acclaimed books *Paper Dolls and Paper Airplanes: Therapeutic Exercises for Sexually Traumatized Children* (with Crisci & Lay, 1997), *Creative Interventions for Troubled Children & Youth* (1999), *Creative Interventions for Children of Divorce (2006), and Creative Interventions for Bereaved Children* (2006). She has also edited the books *Assessment and Treatment Activities for Children, Adolescents*, and *Families: Practitioners Share Their Most Effective Techniques* (Volumes One through Three) and *Creative Family Therapy Techniques: Play, Art, and Expressive Activities to Engage Children in Family Sessions.*

Introduction

This publication is part of a series of books to help children in therapy cope with challenging issues. (For further information on the series, please visit www.lianalowenstein.com.) This version targets children aged 4–7 coping with divorce, though older children may benefit as well.

This book helps children gradually confront and process their issues with the help of Cory, the central character in the story (which is referred to as Cory's Story). Cory is presented as androgynous so both boys and girls can relate. Therapeutic games, art, puppets, and other playful activities are incorporated to lower the threat level of therapy and engage children in treatment. Questions and re-enforcers are woven throughout the story to captivate and sustain the child's interest in the story, and to evaluate and encourage the child's integration of the material.

An atmosphere of safety must be created in which the child and both parents are made to feel accepted, understood, and respected. A positive therapeutic relationship is the key to a positive outcome in therapy (Shirk & Karver, 2003). Developing a positive rapport and establishing a safe environment for the clients leads to a deeper and more significant level of sharing in sessions.

In divorce cases, parents may strive to win the practitioner's allegiance. In order to be most effective, the practitioner must not become aligned with one parent or get drawn into the conflict. The practitioner should take a neutral stance with the parents and remain focused on the needs of the child. The practitioner can maintain neutrality with parents while still conveying empathy for their pain and respect for their points of view.

Gathering information from both parents prior to seeing the child is an important step in the intervention process. (A Parent Questionnaire is included in Appendix A.) If possible, meet with both parents together, unless there are safety concerns that prohibit the parties from coming into contact. It can still be beneficial to conduct a joint session when there is a high level of conflict between the parents, as this can provide valuable assessment information and set the tone for working collaboratively with both parents. It can be helpful as well to meet with parents separately so they can be candid and not edit their remarks in the presence of the other parent.

Although the focus of the first session with the parents is on rapport building and information gathering, there are a number of important administrative tasks that need to be accomplished. A copy of the divorce papers should be obtained in order to confirm custody. Written consent to treatment must be obtained from both custodial parents. In cases of sole custody, it is clinically beneficial to obtain consent to treatment from the non-custodial parent, to encourage this parent's involvement in therapy and secure support for the child's therapy.

As part of the assessment, it is important to observe each parent separately with the child. Play-based activities can be used to assess the family's ability to work together, their boundaries and structure, their communication style, and their patterns of attachment. Examples of play-based assessment activities for families with young children include The Family Gift (Lowenstein, 2006); Create a Family Collage (Lowenstein, 2010b); and Family Puppet Interviews (Gil, 1994).

There are a number of treatment domains that need to be considered when working with children of divorce. These include the following:

a) Clarify divorce-related misconceptions
b) Facilitate the appropriate expression of feelings
c) Strengthen effective coping skills
d) Reduce the stress of transitioning between two homes
e) Address loyalty conflicts
f) Reduce feelings of parental abandonment
g) Protect and remove the child from parental conflict
h) Eliminate self-blame for the divorce
i) Resolve reunification fantasies
j) Foster the child's healthy relationship with both parents
k) Enhance positive perceptions of self

The interventions in this book address the above treatment issues. Each client's unique treatment needs should be assessed so relevant chapters from this book can be selected.

Periodic sessions can be conducted with the child and each parent to enhance the parent–child relationship and facilitate optimal communication. In-depth family therapy may be needed if there are significant strains in the child's relationship with either parent or if there are ongoing parent–child contact problems. While this book includes some interventions for parent–child sessions, it is beyond the scope of this publication to present a comprehensive family therapy intervention program. Moreover, it is often best for the child's therapist to refrain from doing the intensive family work so the child has a neutral ally.

Comprehensive therapeutic intervention should target specific goals for the parents, including divorce education, reducing parental conflict, and enhancing parenting. These goals can be achieved, in part, through the letters that are included in this book, that are intended to be given to each parent at the end of each session. (The letter can be emailed or mailed to the non-attending parent.) Separate sessions with parents can be scheduled as needed to review the letters and address parent–child issues. However, as mentioned above, if there are major problems in the parent–child relationship, parental functioning level, or if the parents are engaged in ongoing conflict, it may be more appropriate for the parents to be referred to other mental health professionals (i.e., individual therapist, family therapist, group therapy, parent education programs, divorce mediation, parenting coordinator) and for the child's therapist to collaborate with members of the treatment team.

In some cases, divorced parents who seek therapy for their children have a hidden agenda to use the therapy information in legal proceedings. It is not the role of the child's therapist to conduct a custody and access assessment, or to make recommendations to the court. The child's therapist should avoid becoming involved in the custody proceedings. It is therefore strongly recommended that both parents be asked to sign a Custody/Access Dispute Contract before proceeding with any clinical assessment or treatment. (See Appendix B.) While this contract is not legally binding, it is clinically beneficial to have this document signed by both parents.

Clinical judgment must be used when deciding what information to share with the parents regarding the content of the child's sessions. In some instances, particularly high-conflict divorce cases, it is best to refrain from sharing detailed information. This allows the child to more freely express thoughts and feelings without worrying about how their information will be perceived by the child's parents. On the other hand, it is often clinically helpful to the child for some information to be shared with the parents, so the parents can better understand the child's perspective and respond more appropriately. If the decision is made to share information, always make an effort to communicate equally with both parents regarding their child's treatment.

This book is geared to children of divorce who have ongoing contact with both parents. The story can be modified for various scenarios, including children who are estranged from one parent, or children with same-sex parents. Additional chapters can be added as needed to help children cope with issues such as a new partner or remarriage, a parent's sadness, moving, and so on. **If adaptations are made to this publication, be sure to maintain the following copyright notice on every page: © Original Copyright Liana Lowenstein 2013; All Rights Reserved.**

When making modifications to the book, keep in mind that preschool children are concrete thinkers and do not yet have the ability for abstract thought. Therefore, use clear, concrete, and simple language.

Cory's Story serves as a catalyst to process the client's issues. The therapeutic value of the story rests largely on the practitioner's ability to use the intervention as a springboard to explore the child's feelings and experiences. Below are some practical guidelines to aid in the appropriate use of Cory's Story:

- Modify the story to suit the developmental, cultural, familial, and clinical needs of the client. (See the copyright statement above.)

- Gather required materials prior to each session such as colored pencils, markers, paper, scissors, people figurines, two doll houses, balloons, bubbles, playdough, etc.

- Copy the story and parent letters for the clients. (**The book may be reproduced for direct use with clients. Any other use or reproduction is a violation of international copyright laws.**)

- Place the client's copy of Cory's Story in a scrapbook and keep it in a locked storage unit between sessions until the last session, at which point it can be given to the child to keep. (A copy of the scrapbook should be placed in the client's file prior to giving it to the client to take home.)

- Read one chapter of Cory's Story to the child each session. Provide the parents with a copy of the chapter and the corresponding letter to read prior to or during the child's session and process with them as needed.

- Give rewards when the child answers questions from the story. For example, the child can earn tokens, then trade in tokens for a prize from the goodie box once ten tokens have been earned. Or the child can earn Lego or beads and make something once enough have been accumulated. (It can be helpful to provide the child with a Ziploc® bag labeled with the child's name to hold the tokens, Lego, or beads.) Some of the questions evaluate the child's understanding of key concepts from Cory's Story and have a "correct" answer. For these questions, if the child does not provide an appropriate answer to the particular question, re-read the relevant segment of the story to provide the child the opportunity to earn a token for the appropriate answer.

- Write the child's responses to the questions using a colored fine tip marker or a colored pencil. (Allow the child to choose the color.) Write the child's responses to the questions verbatim.

- Follow the same structure every session so that the client becomes comfortable with the predictability of the therapeutic process. For example, read Cory's Story and complete the chapter activities, then allow the child to trade in tokens for a prize. Devote the second part of the session to child-led play.

- Prepare the client well in advance of the last session. Clearly explain to the child how and when therapy will end. The Cookie Jar activity (Lowenstein, 2011) is geared especially to young children to help prepare them for termination.

Practitioners working with young children of divorce should have clinical training and a sound knowledge base in the following areas: child development; language acquisition; attachment theory; psychopathology; the developmental impact of divorce on children; risk factors for children's healthy adjustment to divorce; working with high-conflict families of divorce; the continuum of child–parent relationships after divorce; psychological tasks for children of divorce; and play therapy for children of divorce. A list of suggested readings and professional training associations is provided at the end of the book for those who wish to broaden their knowledge.

CHAPTER OVERVIEW
Getting To Know Each Other

Objectives
· Verbalize positive feelings about therapy
· Increase ability to communicate openly
· Identify with Cory to reduce feelings of isolation

Materials
· Scrapbook
· Tokens (or coins, carnival tickets, beads, or Lego)
· Box filled with inexpensive prizes
· Ziploc® bag labeled with the client's name to hold the tokens (or beads or Lego)
· Colored fine tip markers or colored pencils
· Camera (optional)
· Two balloons
· Three copies of "Getting to Know Each Other" (one copy for the child's scrapbook, one copy for each parent)
· Letter for parents (one copy for each parent)

Advance Preparation
Blow up and knot two balloons. (Only one balloon is needed for the session but it is a good idea to have two in case one pops.)

Discussion
The focus of the first chapter is to introduce Cory (the main character) to the child. Through the story, the child realizes that he is not alone—that there are other kids whose parents are divorced.

This chapter also begins the rapport-building process so the child will feel comfortable coming to therapy and being open and expressive during sessions. The Balloon Bounce game is an engaging rapport-building technique. Questions should be easy for the child to answer, require minimal emotional risk-taking, and should focus on getting acquainted. Examples include "What is your favorite color?" and "What is your favorite movie?"

The "special handshake" is another strategy that facilitates a positive rapport. Create a handshake that is easy for both you and the child to remember. (It is best to use the same handshake with all clients to avoid confusion!) The handshake can be used to greet the client at each session, and re-engage the child in therapy.

Cory's Story can be introduced as follows: "Today we're going to begin reading Cory's Story. This is a story about a kid who is kind of like you. As I read the story to you, it's important that you have on your listening ears because there are questions for you to answer about the story. You get a token for every question you answer. Each time you get ten tokens, you can pick something from my prize box."

It is recommended that the child be given a scrapbook in the first session in which to place Cory's Story as well as other activities completed during sessions. The scrapbook has several benefits: it allows the child to see the progression of sessions; it provides immediate tangible reinforcement of each therapeutic success; and it gives the child a lasting record to have once therapy is terminated.

It can be helpful to take a picture of the client in the first session to put on the cover of his scrapbook. This personalizes the scrapbook and serves as a visual reminder for the child in later years when he is looking through the scrapbook.

Getting To Know Each Other

This is a story about a super-duper kid named Cory. Cory loves to build forts, color pictures, and jump in rain puddles. Cory loves pizza, chocolate, and broccoli—yup, that's right, Cory loves broccoli!

What is the name of the kid in this story?

Cory loves to build forts, color pictures, and jump in rain puddles. What are some of your favorite things to do?

Cory loves pizza, chocolate, and broccoli. What are some of your favorite foods?

Cory had lots of fun, happy times, like when Cory went to the zoo. But sometimes there were sad times, like when Cory's parents got a divorce (that means they stopped living together). But we will talk more about that later. Let's get back to Cory. You see, there is something extra super-duper special about Cory. Cory can fly! Well, that's not true, but Cory thought it would be so, so, so cool to have super powers and be able to fly!

Cory had lots of fun, happy times, like when Cory went to the zoo. Tell about something fun that you got to do.

Are Cory's parents divorced (did they stop living together)?

Cory thought it would be so, so, so cool to fly. If you had any super power, what do you wish you could do? Pretend that you have this super power right now and show what it looks like.

Cory went to see a lady named Ana. Some kids called her Ana Banana! And some kids just called her Banana! Cory thought that was so funny, so Cory decided to call her Banana too!

Banana is a therapist. That means Banana's job is to help kids with their problems and upset feelings. Banana said therapy is a place to get help for upset feelings and learn ways to feel better. Banana explained they would be doing some talking and some playing.

What is the name of Cory's therapist?

What is the name of your therapist?

Is therapy a place to get help for upset feelings and learn ways to feel better?

Banana said, "Let's play a game to get to know each other better. It's called Balloon Bounce. I'm going to throw the balloon in the air and we're going to work together to try to keep it in the air without it touching the ground. When the balloon falls to the ground we're going to freeze our bodies. I'm going to ask you a question to get to know you better. Once you answer the question, you get to ask me something to get to know me better. (You can ask me the same question I asked you, or you can make up your own question that will help you get to know me better.) We'll play five rounds so we can ask each other five questions to get to know each other better."

You can play Balloon Bounce too! It will be a fun way for you and your therapist to get to know each other.

After you play Balloon Bounce, say one thing you learned about your therapist.

Banana taught Cory a special handshake. Banana said, "All kids who come here learn this special handshake. Each time you come, we will greet each other with this special handshake. It will be our special way of saying hello!" Cory loved the special handshake. Cory was excited to come back to therapy to do the special handshake with Banana!

You can learn the special handshake too! Then each time you come, you and your therapist can say hello with the special handshake.

Dear Parents,

Today I started reading **Cory's Story** to your child. Cory's Story will help your child cope better with the divorce. I will read a different chapter of Cory's Story to your child over the next several sessions. Each chapter will highlight a different theme or issue.

The focus of this chapter is on introducing Cory to your child. Your child will relate to Cory and realize that he is not the only one whose parents are divorced. Although the issue of divorce is introduced in this chapter, it is not the focus as children need to be eased into talking about difficult issues. This chapter helps to build a positive therapeutic rapport so your child will feel comfortable coming to therapy and being open and expressive during sessions.

Thank you for bringing your child to therapy. You have already taken an important step in helping your child. Below are some ways **you can help** make therapy beneficial for your child:

— Tell your child that therapy is a place to get help with problems and upset feelings.

— Let your child know that he can talk about anything in therapy and he will not get in trouble for anything he says.

— Many children find it uncomfortable when their parents ask them to talk about details of their sessions. It is helpful to ask your child a more general question, such as, "How was your session today?" Your child can then decide what he feels like sharing.

— Try not to force or bribe your child to come to therapy or give punishments if your child refuses to come to sessions. If there is a problem bringing your child to therapy, please contact me to consult.

— Contact me prior to the session if there are significant updates so I am kept informed and can plan accordingly. It is best to contact me when your child cannot overhear the conversation so we can freely discuss concerns. Whenever possible, please contact me well in advance of the session, rather than at the time of the appointment, so your child can benefit from the full session time.

— Coach your child to practice coping skills learned in sessions.

Divorce is painful for everyone in the family, including children. However, children can adjust to divorce in a healthy way if you make the decisions and take the actions that will nurture your children's resilience. The written information you receive from me, and the goals you achieve in therapy, will help you support your child through the divorce so he can grow up to be a healthy, well-functioning adult.

Attached is a copy of the chapter from today's session so you can better understand what was covered.

CHAPTER OVERVIEW
Feelings

Objectives
- Increase the ability to identify and express various emotional states
- Identify the connection between feelings and facial expressions

Materials
- Client's scrapbook
- Tokens (or coins, carnival tickets, beads, or Lego)
- Box filled with inexpensive prizes
- Client's Ziploc® bag
- Colored fine tip markers or colored pencils
- Feeling Squares (included)
- Scissors
- Hand-held, non-breakable mirror (optional)
- Three copies of "Feelings" (one copy for the child's scrapbook, one copy for each parent)
- Letter for parents (one copy for each parent)

Advance Preparation
Cut out the Feeling Squares.

Discussion
This chapter provides young children with the opportunity to develop a vocabulary for their feelings and to practice expressing those feelings. Children typically enjoy the Guess Which Hand game.

Children are generally able to understand the concept of feeling happy, sad, or angry. Other feelings, such as guilty or jealous, need to be explained, using examples that the child understands. For example, "Guilty means when you know you did something wrong. Like, if you tell a lie and you feel bad about it." Once the child comprehends each of the Feeling Squares, he is better able to ascribe feelings to situations in his own life. As the child talks about his feelings, the therapist can reflect the child's feelings, ask the child to elaborate, and praise the child for his openness. When it is the therapist's turn to share, the therapist can tailor his own responses in a way that would be therapeutically beneficial to the child. It is helpful to have a mirror available so the child can see his facial expressions.

Some of the feeling words can be omitted from the game if playing with younger children who cannot grasp the concepts, or who have difficulty maintaining focus. Fidgety children may benefit from playing the game standing up.

Once the game has been played and the child is able to give appropriate responses for the various emotional states, it can be helpful to ask exploratory questions to gather additional assessment information. For example:

When you get a present, do you feel happy, sad, mad, or scared?

When your toy breaks, do you feel happy, sad, mad, or scared?

When you are with your mom, do you feel happy, sad, mad, or scared?

When you are with your dad, do you feel happy, sad, mad, or scared?

When you leave your mom to go to your dad, do you feel happy, sad, mad, or scared?

When you leave your dad to go to your mom, do you feel happy, sad, mad, or scared?

When your mom and dad argue, do you feel happy, sad, mad, or scared?

When you get a treat, do you feel happy, sad, mad, or scared?

The Guess Which Hand game can be played in subsequent sessions as a "check-in" activity prior to reading each new chapter of Cory's Story. The therapist or child can select two feelings to play two rounds of the game. As children master the game and feel more comfortable in therapy, they typically take greater emotional risks and reveal deeper experiences.

Feelings

Welcome back to the story! Today we're going to talk about feelings. Banana explained, "Everyone has feelings. Sometimes we feel happy, like when we get a present. Sometimes we feel sad, like when a friend moves far away. Sometimes we feel angry, like when we don't get what we want. And sometimes we feel scared, like when we have a bad dream. Everyone has feelings. Happy, sad, angry, and scared are some of the ways we sometimes feel. We're going to play a game today to help us talk about feelings. It's called Guess Which Hand. Let's follow the instructions to learn how to play." Cory was excited to play the game!

You can play the game too. Follow the instructions below to play the game with your therapist.

Guess Which Hand

Place the Feeling Squares face up on the table. Your therapist will pick up a Feeling Square (i.e., happy), fold it several times to form a small paper clump, and place it in one hand. Your therapist will put her hands behind her back, and move the folded Feeling Square from hand to hand a few times. Then you have to guess which hand is holding the Feeling Square. If you guess the correct hand, you and your therapist take turns telling a time you experienced the feeling. You get a point for telling about the feeling, plus a bonus point for guessing the correct hand. You get an extra bonus point for showing with your face and body what the feeling looks like.

At the end of the game, trade in points for a prize: 1-15 points = 1 prize; 16 or more points = 2 prizes. Your therapist will write down your answers below:

I feel happy when: _____

I feel sad when: _____

I feel angry when: _____

I feel scared when: _____

I feel guilty when: _____

I feel jealous when: _____

I feel frustrated when: _____

I feel disappointed when: _____

I feel worried when: _____

I feel confused when: _____

I feel proud when: _____

I feel loved when: _____

Cory liked the game—it was fun! And Cory felt better talking about feelings.

Did Cory feel better talking about feelings?

Take turns with your therapist saying something you learned about each other.

Feeling Squares

HAPPY
Something good
happens

SAD
Something upsets you

ANGRY
You don't like what
happened

SCARED
Something scary or
dangerous is happening

GUILTY
You know you did
something wrong

JEALOUS
Someone has something
you want

FRUSTRATED
You try to do something
but you can't do it

DISAPPOINTED
You want something to
happen and it doesn't

WORRIED
You think something
bad is going to happen

CONFUSED
You don't know the
answer to something

PROUD
You do something well

LOVED
Someone cares about
you a lot

Dear Parents,

It is important for children to develop a feelings vocabulary and to learn healthy ways to express their emotions. **You can help** your child by modeling the healthy expression of feelings. If you express your emotions in an open and healthy way, it will help your child express emotions in an open and healthy way! Here are some specific ideas to help your child express emotions in a healthy way:

— Label your emotions to help your child learn a feelings vocabulary. For example, say, "I feel frustrated because I am trying to open this jar and I can't" or "I feel proud of you for playing so nicely with your friend."

— Talk with your child about how you are feeling, but only share information that is appropriate and helpful for your child. For example, do not share feelings pertaining to the custody/access dispute or other "adult" issues. Most importantly, do not badmouth the other parent. I repeat, do not badmouth the other parent!

— Label your child's feelings and invite open discussion. For example, say, "You look angry right now. Tell me about your angry feelings."

— Make talk time part of your nightly routine. For example, each night at bedtime, do Pillow Talk: Sit or lie beside your child in bed, and ask him about his day. For example, ask, "How was your day today? Was it a happy face day or a sad face day? What happened to make it a happy face day or a sad face day?" If your child talks about something upsetting that happened, validate his feelings. For example, say, "It is upsetting when other kids say something mean to you." Don't feel like you have to make it all better—simply listening to your child and validating his feelings is what your child needs most from you. And try to do Pillow Talk every night at bedtime. (Note: For some children, Pillow Talk may trigger upsetting feelings before sleep and, as such, "cuddle/talk time" should happen earlier in the day.)

Attached is a copy of the chapter from today's session so you can better understand what was covered.

CHAPTER OVERVIEW
Marriage and Divorce

Objectives

- Verbalize an understanding of marriage and divorce
- Identify common feelings and reactions associated with divorce
- Learn and implement healthy coping skills

Materials

- Client's scrapbook
- Client's Ziploc® bag
- Tokens (or coins, carnival tickets, beads, or Lego)
- Box filled with inexpensive prizes
- Colored fine tip markers or colored pencils
- People figurines (male and female adults and children)
- Bride and groom figurines (optional)
- Two dollhouses
- Three copies of "Marriage and Divorce" (one copy for the child's scrapbook, one copy for each parent)
- Letter for parents (one copy for each parent)

Discussion

Although parents may have explained the divorce to their children, children benefit from an appropriate explanation from a neutral person. This chapter explains divorce and related issues, and normalizes feelings related to the divorce. The learning is enhanced by having the child demonstrate the concepts with toys. Ideally, the practitioner will have appropriate toys on hand. If people figurines and two dollhouses are unavailable, the child can draw or create with art supplies or playdough.

The letter for parents helps parents understand the importance of providing the child with a simple, direct explanation of divorce. Some parents may benefit from a session with the practitioner that specifically helps them define divorce for their child in an agreed-upon way. Additionally, children need to discuss/ask questions about divorce as they mature and as they are ready to speak more openly about it, so it is helpful to explain to parents that these discussions will need to be repeated.

Marriage and divorce are abstract concepts that can be difficult for young children to understand. Children will be better able to grasp the concepts by looking at family photos depicting the family's history. This can include photos of the parents' wedding, the child's baby pictures, and photos of special family occasions (both before and after the marital separation). It is recommended to have conjoint sessions (one with the child and mother and one with the child and father) to look through and discuss the photos, and to select a few to put in the child's scrapbook. The parents can write brief descriptions under each photo, highlighting information that is meaningful to the child. These parent–child sessions should be scheduled after the session in which the child learns about marriage and divorce. The practitioner can meet with the parents ahead of time to ensure that they can discuss the photos appropriately with their child.

Discussing the family's history via photos also helps children put the divorce in perspective. It can help them see that they have experienced many good moments in the past, and they have many years ahead to have fun and happy times with their families.

Some parts of this chapter may need to be modified to fit the child's situation. For example, if the child was adopted, the question "Were your mom and dad happy when you were born?" should be changed to "Were your mom and dad happy when you were adopted?" Modifications can be made if the parents are a gay/lesbian couple. Modifications can also be made if one parent moved a considerable distance away or if contact with a parent was terminated. (These issues are addressed in the chapter "Coping with Upset Feelings.")

Teaching stress management is an important component of treatment. Diaphragmatic breathing is a particularly helpful relaxation strategy. Cookie Breathing is a fun way to teach children diaphragmatic breathing. The parents will need to learn Cookie Breathing so they can coach the child to practice at home and cue the child to use the strategy when the child needs to de-stress. The practitioner can follow up in subsequent sessions to see if the child has "become an expert" at Cookie Breathing. Parents may benefit from learning diaphragmatic breathing, themselves, given the stress they may be experiencing.

Marriage and Divorce

Welcome back to the story! Today we're going to talk about marriage and divorce. Let's begin by learning about Cory's family. At first, Cory's mom and dad didn't even know each other! Then they met. When Cory's mom and dad met, they liked each other a lot.

Did Cory's mom and dad like each other when they first met?

Your mom and dad liked each other when they first met. Use the toys or things in this room to show that your mom and dad liked each other when they first met.

After Cory's mom and dad met, they spent time together. After Cory's mom and dad met, they had a lot of fun together. Cory's mom and dad liked each other so much that they wanted to be together. So, after a while, they decided to get married. Married is when two people decide to become husband and wife because they want to be together.

Is married when two people decide to become husband and wife because they want to be together?

Use the toys or things in this room to show what married looks like.

Mom and Dad had a family together. They had a beautiful baby who they named Cory. Mom and Dad were so happy when Cory was born. They loved their little baby so much! Mom cuddled baby Cory in her arms and said, "Cory, I love you so, so, so much!" Dad cuddled baby Cory in his arms and said, "Cory, I love you so, so, so much!" Cory and Mom and Dad had lots of fun together. Cory and Mom and Dad went to the park together. Cory and Mom and Dad went to the zoo together. Cory and Mom and Dad went on little trips together.

Were Cory's mom and dad happy when baby Cory was born?

Were your mom and dad happy when you were born?

When Cory was a baby, Cory lived with Mom and Dad in the same home. Use the toys or things in this room to show who you lived with when you were born.

At first, Cory's mom and dad were happy together. But after a while, they started to have big disagreements. They tried hard to be happy together again, but no matter how hard they tried, they could not be happy together anymore. So Cory's mom and dad made a very big and difficult decision. Cory's mom and dad decided to get a divorce. Divorce happens when parents cannot live happily together. Divorce is when parents decide not to be married anymore and to live separately from now on. So Cory's mom and dad stopped living together in the same home. Mom lived in one home and Dad lived in another home. Sometimes Cory felt sad that Mom and Dad were divorced. When Cory felt sad, Mom and Dad would give Cory extra cuddles and this helped Cory feel better.

Does divorce mean that parents decide not to be married anymore and to live separately from now on?

Did Cory's mom and dad get a divorce because they could not live happily together anymore?

How come your mom and dad got a divorce and stopped living together?

Your mom lives in one home. Your dad lives in another home. Use the toys or things in this room to show that your mom lives in one home and your dad lives in another home.

When parents get divorced some kids spend lots of time with their mom and lots of time with their dad. Some kids spend lots of time with one parent, and a little time with their other parent. Some kids live with one parent and don't see their other parent. Use the toys or things in this room to show what it's like for you.

All kids feel worried and upset sometimes. But after Cory's parents got a divorce, Cory felt more worried and upset. Banana said, "When you are feeling worried or upset, you can do something to feel better. One way to feel better is to do Cookie Breathing. It's a special way of breathing that can help you feel calm. Let's follow the instructions below to learn how to do it."

Banana taught Cory Cookie Breathing. You can learn Cookie Breathing too! Follow the instructions below to learn how to do it.

Cookie Breathing
Step 1: Put your hand on your tummy, where your belly button is. Slowly breathe in and out. When you breathe in, your hand should move out (away from your tummy). When you breathe out, your hand should move in (toward your tummy). Breathe in and out like this 5 times.

Step 2: Continue this special way of breathing, but now when you breathe in, do it through your nose for 4 seconds, and when you breathe out, do it through your mouth for 4 seconds. To help you do this, pretend that you are looking at a yummy batch of chocolate chip cookies that just came out of the oven. (Or pick your favorite kind of cookie.) As you breathe in, smell those yummy cookies! But they're hot, so you have to blow on them to cool them down. As you breathe out, blow on the cookies to cool them down.

Remember:
Smell the cookies: Breathe in through your nose for 4 seconds, tummy moves out.

Blow on the cookies: Breathe out through your mouth for 4 seconds, tummy moves in.

Do Cookie Breathing until your body feels calm.

Cookie Breathing helped Cory relax. Banana said, "If you do Cookie Breathing at bedtime, it will relax your body and help you sleep better. When you get good at it, you will know how to use Cookie Breathing to help yourself feel better." Cory wanted to sleep better. Cory wanted to feel better. So Cory decided to do Cookie Breathing each night at bedtime.

You can practice Cookie Breathing at home too. Invite your mom/dad into the therapy room and teach Cookie Breathing to your mom/dad. Your mom/dad will help you practice Cookie Breathing each night at bedtime.

Dear Parents,

Explaining divorce to children is a difficult and sensitive process. You may have already provided your child with an appropriate explanation, or you may have avoided the topic because it was too painful. Even if you have already explained the divorce to your child, he can benefit from the explanation provided in this session and with the opportunity to play it out with toys.

One of the most difficult aspects of explaining divorce to children is dealing with the issue of blame. It is emotionally damaging for the child when a parent tells the child the other parent is to blame for the divorce and communicates that the child should be angry with the other parent. An explanation like "We could not live happily together anymore" is simple and truthful, and prevents blaming either parent. **You can help** by repeating this explanation and by refraining from making any blaming statements about the other parent.

If your child reports to you that the other parent has made blaming or nasty remarks about you, one response to say is, "Divorce is hard for everyone and sometimes we say things when we're upset that are not really true." This may be difficult to do when you are feeling angry with the other parent for saying negative things about you, but try your very best!

Divorce is stressful for all family members, including children. Teaching children coping strategies equips them to manage their stress. Diaphragmatic breathing is a particularly helpful relaxation strategy. Cookie Breathing is a fun way to teach children this special way of breathing. However, children will only learn the strategy if they practice it regularly at home. **You can help** by coaching your child to do Cookie Breathing each night at bedtime. It is helpful to implement diaphragmatic breathing at bedtime as it calms the child's body in preparation for sleep. So make Cookie Breathing a part of your bedtime routine, for example: Bathe, put on pajamas, brush teeth, read a bedtime story, do Cookie Breathing. You can do Cookie Breathing along with your child—it will reduce your stress level too!

Once your child has learned Cookie Breathing, you can help your child do it when he needs to de-stress. It is helpful to follow this three-step process:

a) Pay attention to the signs that your child is getting overly angry or anxious, and name what you see: "You just started yelling, it looks like you're getting very angry."

b) Coach your child to use Cookie Breathing to get calm (do Cookie Breathing too so your child can follow your lead): "Let's do Cookie Breathing to help you get calm."

c) Praise your child: "You just did a great job doing Cookie Breathing to calm down."

Attached is a copy of the chapter from today's session so you can better understand what was covered.

CHAPTER OVERVIEW
Families

Objectives
- Verbalize an understanding of different kinds of families
- Identify perceptions of family members
- Articulate that all families have happy and sad times

Materials
- Client's scrapbook
- Client's Ziploc® bag
- Tokens (or coins, carnival tickets, beads, or Lego)
- Box filled with inexpensive prizes
- Colored fine tip markers or colored pencils
- People figurines (multiple males and females of various ages including children and elderly)
- Two dollhouses (or two photos of two different houses)
- Camera (optional)
- Three copies of "Families" (one copy for the child's scrapbook, one copy for each parent)
- Letter for parents (one copy for each parent)

Discussion
Children of divorce often feel stigmatized. They may wonder if there is something wrong with their family because it does not fit within the cultural norm. Children may believe that a "normal" family consists of a mom and dad and brothers and sisters living together. Helping children understand that there are many different types of family configurations can counter these negative feelings. Defining for children that families are people who love and care for each other is also important.

The practitioner can demonstrate to the child various family configurations using people figurines and doll houses. Some examples of family configurations are below:

Mom and Dad and child (or children) all live together

Mom and a child (or children)

Dad and a child (or children)

Two moms and a child (or children)

Two dads and a child (or children)

A family with no children

A family with a stepparent

Mom and Dad live in separate homes, and the child (or children) spends some time with Mom, and some time with Dad

As young children may feel confused or overwhelmed learning about many types of family configurations, it is recommended to choose three to show the child, and show the child's particular family configuration last. The child can then portray his own family configuration with the people figurines and doll houses. This helps the child make sense of and process the information. Once the child has portrayed his family configuration with the people figurines, it can be helpful to take a picture for the client's scrapbook, and add a brief descriptor.

This chapter also assesses the child's perceptions of family members, including who the child believes is most happy, sad, angry, helpful, and playful. This provides valuable information regarding family roles and dynamics. The practitioner can use this information to guide the direction of treatment.

An additional goal of this chapter is to show that it is normal for all families to experience negative and positive life events. This puts the divorce into context and reduces feelings of shame and isolation. The client "plays out" the experiences with people figurines, which facilitates communication and externalization. The practitioner can ask exploratory questions about the "happy and sad times" to encourage further verbalization. It can be helpful to take photographs as the child reenacts the sad and happy times with the figurines, and to place these photographs in the client's scrapbook, with brief descriptors.

Families

Welcome back to the story! Today we're going to talk about families. Let's begin by talking about Cory's family. After Cory's mom and dad got divorced, Mom lived in one home and Dad lived in another home. Cory spent some time with Mom and some time with Dad. Cory worried that they were no longer a family. Cory worried that their family was weird or bad. Banana said, "Cory, there are different kinds of families. I'm going to show you with the toys a few different kinds of families. Let's see if you can guess which kind of family you live in."

You and your therapist can do this too. Your therapist will use the toys to show a few different kinds of families. See if you can guess which kind of family you live in.

Banana said, "There are different kinds of families. No kind of family is good or bad, just different. So don't worry, there is nothing weird or bad about your family." Hearing this helped Cory feel better.

Are there different kinds of families?

Is there something weird or bad about Cory's family?

Is there something weird or bad about your family?

Let's get to know the people in your family better. Use the people figurines to answer the questions below:

Point to the people in your family who feel happy. What makes them feel happy?

Point to the people in your family who feel sad. What makes them feel sad?

Point to the people in your family who feel angry. What makes them feel angry?

Point to the people in your family who help you when you have a problem or worry. What do they do to help you when you have a problem or worry?

Point to the people in your family who play with you. What do you and these people like to play together?

It helped Cory to understand that there are different kinds of families, and no kind of family is good or bad, just different. Cory wondered if divorced families are sadder. Banana explained, "Cory, all families have happy times, and all families have sad times. There are times when you feel happy and times when you feel sad. There are times when your mom and dad feel happy, and times when your mom and dad feel sad. When you or your mom or dad feels sad, know that things will get better and that you and your mom and dad will feel happy again." Cory felt better knowing that when there are sad times, there will be happy times again.

Use the toys or things in this room to show a sad time with your family.

Use the toys or things in this room to show a happy time with your family.

Dear Parents,

Children of divorce often wonder if there is something wrong with their family because it does not fit within the cultural norm. Helping children understand that there are many different types of family configurations can counter these negative feelings. **You can help** your child by pointing out different family configurations of people you know (especially your child's peers). It can also be helpful to look at photos from when you were younger and talk about the family you grew up in. Another helpful idea is to look at family albums or magazines and have the child point out various family configurations, such as a family with a mom and dad and three kids, or a family with a pet, etc. Or at the park, ask the child to try and identify who is in each family. For example, say, "See the little boy on the swing? Is he here all by himself or with someone from his family? How do you know that person is his dad?" and so on.

You play an important role in helping your child feel secure within your family. Important messages to convey to your child can include "Even though we are divorced, we are still your family" and "Families are people who love and care about each other—you have a mom and dad who love you and take care of you."

Attached is a copy of the chapter from today's session so you can better understand what was covered.

CHAPTER OVERVIEW
Two Homes

Objectives
- Articulate positive and negative feelings about living in two homes
- Reduce the stress of transitioning between two homes

Materials
- Client's scrapbook
- Client's Ziploc® bag
- Tokens (or coins, carnival tickets, beads, or Lego)
- Box filled with inexpensive prizes
- Colored fine tip markers or colored pencils
- Coloring supplies such as markers or crayons
- Two large sheets of paper
- Three copies of "Two Homes" (one copy for the child's scrapbook, one copy for each parent)
- Letter for parents (one copy for each parent)

Discussion
Transitioning between two homes can be difficult for children. They may miss the parent they are apart from or experience separation anxiety. They must adapt to changing schedules and physical spaces, and decide what items should be with them in each home. This chapter uses an engaging and active game to help children discuss and process their feelings about going back and forth between two homes.

This chapter gathers information regarding the child's positive and negative experiences with each parent. The information collected can be used to develop additional treatment goals for the family. Clinical judgment must be used regarding any concerning information disclosed by the child. (That is, should the concern be addressed with the parent individually, via a conjoint session with the child and parent, or, in more extreme cases, should it be reported to the child welfare authorities?)

When young children are concerned, the onus for reducing the stress of transitioning between two homes rests largely with the parents. Therefore, a number of practical suggestions for easing transition stress are presented in the letter to the parents.

Two Homes

Welcome back to the story! Today we're going to talk about having two homes. Cory's mom lives in one home. Cory's dad lives in another home. Sometimes Cory is with Mom. Sometimes Cory is with Dad. It's hard for Cory to go back and forth between two homes. It's hard for Cory to pack a bag and bring stuff from one home to the other home. It's hard for Cory to sleep in two different places. When Cory is with Mom, Cory misses Dad. When Cory is with Dad, Cory misses Mom.

Does Cory have two homes?

Do you have two homes?

What does Cory find hard about living in two homes?

What do you find hard about living in two homes?

There are some things Cory likes about living in two homes. Cory gets to have fun, special time with Mom, and fun, special time with Dad. Cory gets to have some of "two things." Like, Cory gets to have two toothbrushes: One toothbrush at Mom's, and one toothbrush at Dad's. When it's Cory's birthday, Cory gets one birthday cake at Mom's, and one birthday cake at Dad's. Cory has two favorite kinds of cookies: A favorite kind of cookie at Mom's, and a favorite kind of cookie at Dad's. But Cory has one special thing that stays with Cory, no matter what—Cory's favorite stuffed animal, Softie! Softie goes with Cory to Mom's, and Softie goes with Cory to Dad's. Cory sleeps with Softie every night, at Mom's and at Dad's. Cory loves Softie!

What does Cory like about living in two homes?

What do you like about living in two homes?

Does Cory sleep with Softie at Mom's and at Dad's?

Do you have something special you sleep with every night?

Banana said, "Cory, we're going to play a game to help us talk about Mom's home, Dad's home. Let's follow the instructions to play the game."

You can play the game too. Follow the instructions below.

Mom's Home, Dad's Home
Draw a picture of Mom's home, and on another piece of paper, draw a picture of Dad's home. Put the picture of Mom's home on one side of the room. Put the picture of Dad's home on the other side of the room.

Hop on your right foot from Dad's home to Mom's home. Tell about something fun you did with Mom.

Hop on your right foot from Mom's home to Dad's home. Tell about something fun you did with Dad.

Walk in slow motion from Dad's home to Mom's home. Say where you sleep at Mom's home.

Walk in slow motion from Mom's home to Dad's home. Say where you sleep at Dad's home.

Hop like a bunny from Dad's home to Mom's home. Say something you like to play with at Mom's home.

Hop like a bunny from Mom's home to Dad's home. Say something you like to play with at Dad's home.

March like a soldier from Dad's home to Mom's home. Tell about something sad or scary that happened at Mom's home.

March like a soldier from Mom's home to Dad's home. Tell about something sad or scary that happened at Dad's home.

Jump like a frog from Dad's home to Mom's home. Tell about the best time ever at Mom's home.

Jump like a frog from Mom's home to Dad's home. Tell about the best time ever at Dad's home.

The Mom's Home, Dad's Home game helped Cory talk about the sad and happy times at Mom's home and Dad's home. Even though it was hard sometimes to go back and forth between two homes, Cory felt good knowing there was lots of love in Mom's home and lots of love in Dad's home.

Does Cory feel good knowing there's lots of love in Mom's home and lots of love in Dad's home?

Do you feel good knowing there's lots of love in your mom's home and lots of love in your dad's home?

Draw two hearts to show there's lots of love in your mom's home and lots of love in your dad's home.

Dear Parents,

One of the most challenging adjustments for children in a divorced family is living in two homes. When they are with one parent, they may miss the other parent. They must adapt to changing schedules and physical spaces, and decide what items should be with them in each home. Even if children only visit one parent for a few hours a week, the children should feel safe and secure in both environments. **<u>You can help</u>** your children cope with transition stress by adhering to the following:

— Work with the other parent to establish a few basic rules and routines that are at both homes such as the same bedtime, the same rule about how much television watching is allowed, etc. However, even if some rules differ, it is not a problem as long as the rules remain consistent in each home. Children learn at a young age that there are different rules in different places—day care, school, grandma's house, etc. Your child can handle another difference, as long as the rules are reliable and consistent in each home.

— Make a calendar with your child. The calendar should include the highlights of his schedule, including all major activities and especially those times when he will be with the other parent. For a younger child who cannot read, use pictures or color codes. Go over the calendar each night.

— Speak positively about the time/activities with the other parent to help prepare/ease the transition for your child. For example, say, "You are going to go to the zoo tomorrow with your mom/dad—I am sure you will have so much fun!"

— Your child should have his own room at each home. If this is not possible, he should have his own space in a room to keep clothes, toys, and other belongings.

— Provide your child with a comfort object that travels back and forth with him between homes (i.e., a favorite stuffed animal, blankie, etc.).

— Together with your child, take photos of your child's favorite people and things (e.g., favorite people, toys, pets) and put them in a mini photo album. The album can travel between the two homes with your child and serve as a source of comfort and security.

— Establish a special greeting at transition periods such as a ten-second hug each time your child returns.

— Create a checklist of items your child needs to bring back and forth to each home, and review this checklist prior to the departure from each home. You can put the checklist on a luggage tag and attach it to the bag that travels back and forth.

— Maintain a communication book that travels to each home with your child. Make sure to keep the content respectful and focused on important information or updates about your child.

— Follow the visitation schedule even when your child feels sick. This reinforces both parents' care-giving abilities.

— Negotiate and follow through with a plan for phone contact when your child is with the other parent. Keep the phone contact brief but nurturing. Don't expect your child to be particularly talkative as many young children find phone contact awkward.

— Try your very best to make pick up and drop off cordial, on time, and upbeat.

Attached is a copy of the chapter from today's session so you can better understand what was covered.

CHAPTER OVERVIEW
Feelings About Divorce

Objectives
- Increase the ability to accurately identify and talk comfortably about feelings related to the divorce
- Learn and implement healthy coping strategies

Materials
- Client's scrapbook
- Client's Ziploc® bag
- Tokens (or coins, carnival tickets, beads, or Lego)
- Box filled with inexpensive prizes
- Colored fine tip markers or colored pencils
- Bubbles
- Camera (optional)
- Three copies of "Feelings about Divorce" (one copy for the child's scrapbook, one copy for each parent)
- Letter for parents (one copy for each parent)

Discussion
Children often feel overwhelmed by mixed emotions associated with divorce. Guilt, anxiety, sadness, and anger are common feelings with which children struggle. Affective expression and modulation skills are important steps toward healthy adaptation to divorce. The playful and physical nature of the activities in this chapter (e.g., popping bubbles and the Stomp, Freeeeze, Cookie Breeeethe technique) are particularly engaging for children. It can be helpful to take photographs of the child popping bubbles and doing Stomp, Freeeeze, Cookie Breeeethe, and to place these photographs in the child's scrapbook with brief descriptors.

Children will identify with many of the feelings expressed by Cory in this chapter. This will help reduce children's sense of isolation. While the story normalizes feelings and facilitates open communication, some children remain guarded, especially regarding painful emotions associated with the divorce. Strategies to encourage openness include asking clients to share which of Cory's feelings they identify with the most, or which feelings they think were the hardest for Cory to talk about.

The Stomp, Freeeeze, Cookie Breeeethe technique can be used across sessions and outside of therapy as a way for the child to modulate anger. If anger management is a more serious presenting issue, then additional activities can be integrated into the child's treatment plan. Recommended anger management interventions for this age group include: If You're Mad and You Know It (Lowenstein, 2002); Volcano of Anger (Cavett, 2010); Mad Maracas (Goodyear-Brown, 2005).

Some clients will be in need of additional interventions to address anxiety. Recommended resources include: *The Worry Wars* by Goodyear-Brown (2010), and the CD/Book *Indigo Ocean Dreams* by Lite (2005).

Feelings About Divorce

Welcome back to the story! Today we're going to talk about feelings related to the divorce. Cory felt a lot of mixed-up, confused feelings about the divorce. One thing Cory felt confused about is why parents divorce. Parents get divorced for many different reasons—grown-up reasons. Cory's mom and dad got divorced because they stopped being happy together. Sometimes Cory wondered if acting naughty or bad made Mom and Dad get divorced. But all kids act naughty or bad sometimes. All kids get in trouble sometimes. Cory's mom and dad did not get divorced because of something Cory did wrong or bad. Divorce is never a kid's fault!

Did Cory's parents get divorced because they stopped being happy together?

Did Cory feel better knowing Mom and Dad did not get divorced because of something Cory did wrong or bad?

Did your parents get divorced because they stopped being happy together?

Did you do something wrong or bad to make your mom and dad get a divorce?

Is divorce ever a kid's fault?

Cory wanted to fix things so Mom and Dad would get married again. But it is not up to kids to fix their parents' marriage. Mom and Dad would be happy if Cory was well behaved all the time. But no kid acts perfectly good all the time. Parents love their children even if they don't behave well. And acting good is not going to make Cory's mom and dad get married again. There is nothing Cory can do to make Mom and Dad get married again.

If Cory acts perfectly good all the time, can this make Mom and Dad get married again?

If you act perfectly good all the time, can this make your mom and dad get married again?

Since the divorce, Cory has been feeling worried a lot. Cory is worried something bad will happen. Cory is worried Mom or Dad will leave and never come back. Sometimes Cory holds on tight to Mom or Dad so they won't leave. All these worried feelings make Cory's tummy hurt. And sometimes Cory has scary dreams.

What makes Cory feel worried?

What makes you feel worried?

Banana said, "Cory, it's normal to feel worried sometimes. Let's see if we can pop your worries away. I'm going to blow some bubbles. Let's pretend the bubbles are your worries. Your job is to pop as many bubbles as you can. Let's see if you can pop your worries away!"

You can pop your worries away too! Your therapist will blow some bubbles. Pretend the bubbles are your worries. Pop as many bubbles as you can. See if you can pop your worries away!

Banana said, "Cory, you did a great job talking about your worries. And you did a super-duper job popping your worries away! What other feelings do you have about the divorce?" Cory said, "I feel sad. Sometimes I cry. Sometimes I try not to cry because I don't want to act like a baby. Sometimes Mom or Dad cries. I try to make them happy when they cry because I don't want Mom or Dad to be sad." Banana said, "Cory, sometimes you or your mom or dad will feel sad. Everyone feels sad sometimes. It's okay to cry when you feel sad. Crying doesn't mean you are acting like a baby. And it's okay for your mom and dad to cry if they feel sad. Crying is a good way to let out sad feelings. Sad feelings don't stay forever."

Is it okay to cry if you feel sad?

Sometimes you will feel sad. Show with your face and body what sad looks like.

What makes you feel sad?

Sometimes you will feel happy. Show with your face and body what happy looks like.

What makes you feel happy?

Cory said, "I also feel angry about the divorce. It's not fair I can't live with Mom and Dad all together in one place. Sometimes I feel very, very angry when I have to leave Mom's to go to Dad's. Sometimes I feel very, very angry when I have to leave Dad's to go to Mom's. I don't like it! I'm angry!"

Cory cannot live with Mom and Dad in one home. Does this make Cory feel angry?

What makes you feel angry about the divorce?

When Cory feels angry, Cory's face gets an angry look. When Cory feels very, very angry, Cory sometimes throws a tantrum. This is when Cory yells and hits and kicks! Banana explained, "Cory, it's okay to feel angry, but it's not okay to yell and hit and kick. When you feel angry, you can calm your body by doing Stomp, Freeeeze, Cookie Breeeethe." Banana described how to do it:

"Stomp your feet 10 times really fast. (Stomp out your angry feelings.) Freeze your body for 10 seconds. Then do Cookie Breathing to calm your body."

Cory said, "Hey, it worked—I stomped out my angry feelings. I did Cookie Breathing to calm my body. I feel calm. I feel better!"

You can do Stomp, Freeeeze, Cookie Breeeethe too! Do it together with your therapist. See if you can stomp out your angry feelings and calm your body.

Dear Parents,

This chapter focuses on emotional reactions typically experienced by children in divorced families. The purpose is to help children understand that their feelings and reactions to the divorce are normal, and to provide them with healthy coping strategies. Here are some issues we covered:

Sadness

Cory's Story normalizes feelings of sadness and conveys the message that it is okay to cry. Some children hide their sadness in order to protect their parents. **You can help** your child by normalizing sad feelings and giving permission to cry and to talk openly. For example, say, "This is a sad time for our family. It is okay to cry when we feel sad. Let's talk about your feelings—what do you feel most sad about?" Although it is difficult to see your child in pain, it is not helpful to pressure your child to be happy when he is not. It is more helpful to listen, validate, and provide physical comfort.

When you openly express your emotions, it gives your child permission to openly express his emotions. However, since some children feel anxious when they see a parent looking very sad or crying, it is important to reassure your child by saying, "Even though I am sad, I will be okay and I will still be able to take care of you." It is also important to reassure your child that you will be able to cope with this crisis. For example, say, "This is a sad time, but I know we will get through it and we will be okay."

Guilt

It is common for children to blame themselves for the divorce. Children need to know that nothing they did or said caused the marital breakup. **You can help** your child by reiterating this message. For example, say, "Nothing you said or did made us get divorced. The divorce is not your fault. The reason for the divorce is because we could not live happily together any more."

In order to counter any bad feelings that your child may have, it is very important to help your child feel that he is a good person. You can do this by focusing on your child's good behavior and by praising your child often. Remember the double rule: For every negative statement you make to your child there should be two positive statements. When praising your child, focus on the desired behavior and be specific. Below are some examples:

I like the way you (asked nicely for a treat).

Thank you for (brushing your teeth when I asked you to).

(You played nicely with your friends today.) That's great.

Worries

Children of divorce tend to have more worries. They may worry their parent will leave and never come back, or they may be concerned about who will take care of them. If your family had to move after the marital separation, your child may worry about having to move again. **You can help** by repeatedly reassuring your child. For example, say, "I am going out for a little while but I will be back soon," or "Even though Mom and Dad live in separate homes, you will still spend lots of time with each of us," or "There will always be a grown-up to take care of you."

Anger

Everyone gets angry at times but some children have difficulty expressing their anger in appropriate ways. They may express their anger through temper tantrums or aggressive behavior. Children need to know that it is okay to be angry but it is not okay to let out anger in hurtful ways. **You can help** your child learn how to express anger appropriately by following these three steps: (1) Validate your child's feelings, i.e., "I know you feel angry right now." (2) Set a limit, i.e., "It's not okay to hit or throw things." (3) Provide an alternative, i.e., "When you feel angry, you can do Stomp, Freeeeze, Cookie Breeeethe."

Although you may feel angry when your child throws a tantrum or behaves aggressively, and your gut reaction may be to respond by punishing, know that this will not help your child learn appropriate ways to behave. Try your very hardest to remain calm and to use the three-step strategy.

Some parents find it hard to respond to children's sadness and anger in the affirming ways suggested above, usually because their parents did not respond to them with sensitivity and understanding. If this is the case for you, try the ideas suggested above, and over time it will get easier. If you continue to struggle, it might be helpful to seek the guidance and support of a mental health professional.

Attached is a copy of the chapter from today's session so you can better understand what was covered.

CHAPTER OVERVIEW
Coping With Upset Feelings

Objectives
- Verbally express feelings related to the divorce
- Learn and implement healthy coping strategies

Materials
- Client's scrapbook
- Client's Ziploc® bag
- Tokens (or coins, carnival tickets, beads, or Lego)
- Box filled with inexpensive prizes
- Colored fine tip markers or colored pencils
- Upsetting Situations (included)
- Scissors
- Crafts to make puppets (see Discussion section below)
- Photo of each parent (see Discussion section below)
- Three copies of "Coping with Upset Feelings" (one copy for the child's scrapbook, one copy for each parent)
- Letter for parents (one copy for each parent)

Advance Preparation
Review the Upsetting Situations, select the ones that are appropriate to the client, and cut them out to make Situation Cards.

Discussion
This chapter helps children cope with typical stressors related to divorce, including loyalty conflicts, visitation issues, dating, a depressed parent, and moving. Variations are included to help children who are dealing with a faraway parent or parental abandonment. The practitioner can select the Situation Cards that are appropriate to the client, and add additional scenarios to ensure that the client's treatment issues are addressed.

The client can create the mom and dad puppets using paper bags, paper plates, or popsicle sticks. Craft supplies can be used to make the faces. Another idea is to request a photo of each parent and to glue each photo onto the paper bag, paper plate, or popsicle stick.

The activity will not necessarily fully address the stressors, but it will normalize the child's feelings and provide a variety of coping strategies. The success of the intervention will be greatly enhanced by engaging the parents in the treatment process, and helping them to adhere to the tips outlined in the letter for parents.

If a parent has moved a considerable distance away but still maintains contact with his child, the practitioner can try to contact the faraway parent via phone, email, Skype, or another video-calling software and engage that parent in the treatment process. The parent can be provided with guidance on ways he can maintain strong relationships with his child from long distances.

Coping With Upset Feelings

Welcome back to the story! Today we're going to talk about what to do with upset feelings. Banana said, "When parents are divorced, things happen that can make kids feel sad, angry, bad, worried, or confused. But you can learn ways to feel better when you have upset feelings. We're going to make mom and dad puppets. Then we will use these puppets to help you feel better when you are upset."

You can make mom and dad puppets too and then use the puppets to help you feel better when you are upset. First, make two puppets: Make a mom and a dad puppet.

Next, your therapist will read some situations and you will use the mom and dad puppets to help you with upset feelings.

After they did the activity with the mom and dad puppets, Cory felt much better. Banana reminded Cory, "Your mom and dad love you very much. They want you to be happy. They want you to know that your feelings are most important. So you can talk to your mom and dad about your feelings, problems, and worries. They will try their best to help you feel better!"

Can Cory talk to Mom and Dad about feelings, problems, and worries?

Can you talk to your mom and dad about your feelings, problems, and worries?

Have the mom and dad puppets say to you: "You can talk to us about your feelings, problems, and worries. We will try our best to help you feel better!"

Upsetting Situations

When you do something fun with Dad, you are excited to tell Mom all about it. But you are worried that telling Mom will make her upset. When you do something fun with Mom, you are excited to tell Dad all about it. But you are worried that telling Dad will make him upset.

It's important for you to know: It's okay to have fun with Mom and Dad. It's okay to tell Mom you had fun with Dad. It's okay to tell Dad you had fun with Mom. You can talk to Mom and Dad about whatever you are feeling. Your feelings are most important!

Have the mom and dad puppets say to you:
You can talk to us about fun times you have.

When you are with Mom, you miss Dad. You are afraid to tell Mom you miss Dad. When you are with Dad, you miss Mom. You are afraid to tell Dad you miss Mom.

It's important for you to know: It's normal and okay to miss Dad when you are not with him. It's normal and okay to miss Mom when you are not with her. You can tell Mom when you miss Dad. You can tell Dad when you miss Mom. You can talk to Mom and Dad about whatever you are feeling. Your feelings are most important!

Have the mom and dad puppets say to you:
You can talk to us about whatever you are feeling. We will try to help you feel better.

It's picture day at school. Mom wants you to wear the sweater she bought you. Dad wants you to wear the sweater he bought you. You are worried if you wear the sweater Mom bought you then Dad will be upset. You are worried if you wear the sweater Dad bought you then Mom will be upset.

It's important for you to know: You don't have to worry about upsetting Mom or Dad. You can do what makes you feel happy.

Have the mom and dad puppets say to you:
You get to choose which sweater to wear. Your feelings are most important!

Mom tells you the divorce is Dad's fault. Dad tells you the divorce is Mom's fault. This makes you feel upset and confused.

It's important for you to know: The divorce is not Mom's fault or Dad's fault. Lots of things happened when Mom and Dad were married that made them both feel unhappy being together. Mom and Dad got a divorce because they decided they couldn't be happy together.

Have the mom and dad puppets say to you:
You don't have to pick sides and blame Mom or Dad for the divorce. You can have happy, loving feelings for us both!

Mom says mean things about Dad. This makes you feel sad, scared, and angry.

It's important for you to know: People may say mean things when they are angry but they can learn better ways to handle angry feelings.

Have the mom puppet say to you:
Sometimes I say mean things about Dad when I feel angry. I am so sorry that this upsets you. I am working on handling my angry feelings in a better way.

Dad says mean things about Mom. This makes you feel sad, scared, and angry.

It's important for you to know: People may say mean things when they are angry but they can learn better ways to handle angry feelings.

Have the dad puppet say to you:
Sometimes I say mean things about Mom when I feel angry. I am so sorry that this upsets you. I am working on handling my angry feelings in a better way.

Mom says she wants you to live with her. Dad says he wants you to live with him. You love Mom and Dad and you want to spend time with each of them.

It's important for you to know: You can love Mom and Dad and spend time with each of them. You don't have to pick one parent to love. The adults will decide what is best for you, and how much time you will spend with each parent.

Have the mom and dad puppets say to you:
You can love us both. We will make sure you get to spend time with each of us.

Dad doesn't show up for a visit. This makes you feel sad and angry.

It's important for you to know: Even if Dad misses a visit, he still loves you very much.

Have the dad puppet say to you:
I am so sorry that I missed our special time together. I love you very much and I am excited to see you soon.

Mom doesn't show up for a visit. This makes you feel sad and angry.

It's important for you to know: Even if Mom misses a visit, she still loves you very much.

Have the mom puppet say to you:
I am so sorry that I missed our special time together. I love you very much and I am excited to see you soon.

Mom has a new friend. She spends lots of time with this new friend. You feel upset when Mom spends time with this new friend instead of playing with you.

It's important for you to know: Even when Mom spends time with her friends, you are still the most important person to Mom. You can talk to Mom about your upset feelings.

Have the mom puppet say to you:
You are the most important person to me. We will still spend lots of time together.

Dad has a new friend. He spends lots of time with this new friend. You feel upset when Dad spends time with this new friend instead of playing with you.

It's important for you to know: Even when Dad spends time with his friends, you are still the most important person to Dad. You can talk to Dad about your upset feelings.

Have the dad puppet say to you:
You are the most important person to me. We will still spend lots of time together.

Dad feels sad. Dad cries a lot. You feel upset and worried when Dad is so sad.

It's important for you to know: Dad is sad about the divorce. But even when Dad is sad, he can still take good care of you. Even when Dad is sad, you can still talk to him about your feelings.

Have the dad puppet say to you:
Even when I am sad, I am okay and I can still take good care of you.

Have the dad puppet say to you:
Even when I am sad, you can talk to me about whatever you are feeling.

Mom feels sad. Mom cries a lot. You feel upset and worried when Mom is so sad.

It's important for you to know: Mom is sad about the divorce. But even when Mom is sad, she can still take good care of you. Even when Mom is sad, you can still talk to her about your feelings.

Have the mom puppet say to you:
Even when I am sad, I am okay and I can still take good care of you.

Have the mom puppet say to you:
Even when I am sad, you can talk to me about whatever you are feeling.

It's your birthday and you feel upset because you can't celebrate it with Mom and Dad together.

It's important for you to know: It's normal to feel sad that you can't celebrate your birthday with Mom and Dad together. But Mom and Dad can each do something special to make sure you have a happy birthday!

Have the mom and dad puppets say to you:
We will do something special to help you have a happy birthday!

You have to move to another home. This makes you feel worried and sad.

It's important for you to know: Moving can be hard, but your therapist will talk to your parents about ways to make it easier.

Have the mom and dad puppets say to you:
We will find ways to make it easier so you won't feel so sad and worried about moving.

Dear Parents,

This chapter will help your child cope with a number of stressors related to the divorce. However, the activity will not be particularly effective unless you commit to putting the emotional needs of your child first. Below are some suggestions on ways **you can help** your child. (Note: Not all the issues below will fit your particular situation, so please refer to the content that is appropriate to your family.)

Tips for Preventing Loyalty Conflicts

Children in divorced families often feel caught in the middle. They may feel they have to take sides and love one parent more than the other. They may feel a need to put their own feelings and needs aside in order to please you. They may feel they have to keep secrets. This loyalty bind is emotionally damaging to children. The following are some suggestions from the book *Making Divorce Easier on Your* Child by Long and Forehand, and from the website www.UpToParents.org:

— Accept and encourage your child's love for the other parent. It is healthy and beneficial for your child to want to talk about and do things for his other parent; allow this to occur.

— Communicate positive feelings about the other parent. For example, once a week share with your child a good quality (or good memory) about the other parent. Or point out a positive quality your child gets from the other parent (e.g., "You have a beautiful smile, just like your dad" or "You have a great singing voice just like your mom").

— Be aware of the subtle, nonverbal messages you convey that could make your child feel caught in a loyalty bind. For example, telling your child to call the other parent but then acting sad or aloof when your child makes the call. Send clear messages that support your child's relationship with the other parent, for example, say, "I want you to talk to Dad/Mom. He/she loves you so much and wants to spend time with you." Make sure your tone of voice and body language send the appropriate signals.

— Don't make your child keep secrets from the other parent or lie for you.

— Don't talk to your child about adult issues such as money problems, child support, and court battles.

— Separate your feelings for the other parent from your child's feelings for the other parent. This may be difficult, but it is an important aspect of how you can help your child adjust to the divorce in a healthy way.

- Encourage and support regular contact between your child and his other parent, and help your child express his love for the other parent. For example, take your child to buy a birthday gift for the other parent, encourage your child to call the other parent with important news, buy a postcard for your child to send to the other parent when you are on vacation, etc.

- Celebrate what your child gets to do with the other parent. For example, say, "I know how excited you are that Dad is coaching your soccer team" or "You and Mom are going to have so much fun on this trip."

- Regularly talk about yourself and the other parent collectively. For example, say, "Dad/Mom and I were talking and saying how proud we are about the progress you have made in swim class."

You may feel you are already doing what is necessary and that the other parent is the one to blame for your child's loyalty binds. However, there are two sides to every pancake! You cannot control the other parent's behavior. You can only control your own behavior and do what is best for your child.

Tips for Helping Your Child Cope When You Start Dating

Every child will react in his own way to a parent's dating after the divorce. However, below is some information about how children are typically affected by parental dating after divorce:

- When a parent begins dating, a child's hope that his parents will reunite is shattered.

- Children are likely to view a date/new partner as a threat to their own relationship with you. They may not voice this concern, either because they lack the cognitive skills to articulate their feelings or because they do not want to displease you.

- It is awkward for children to adjust to having an adult who is not their parent acting in a parenting role.

- Children may experience loyalty conflicts between biological parents and new partners.

- Children fear future rejection if the new relationship does not last.

On the other hand, parental dating after divorce can also offer benefits to children, such as:

— Happier parents mean better moods.

— A role model of a happy adult relationship.

— New people who care about them.

Below are some suggestions on how to help your child adjust to your dating:

— Keep your dating relationships private and away from your child until the relationship is serious. Only you can decide what "serious" means for you. What you should avoid, however, is introducing your child to every person you date after your divorce. If your child attaches to every person you date, he is likely to be hurt and experience loss each time the relationship does not work.

— Make sure the introduction of your new significant other takes place only after you have had a private conversation with your child about the relationship. For a younger child, you can refer to your partner as a "new friend." For example, "I have a new friend who would like to meet you. His/her name is ___. We're all going to go to the park tomorrow." It can be helpful to choose a setting where the focus will be on an activity, not "getting to know each other better."

— Demonstrate with words and action that a new love interest will not undermine your parent–child relationship. Don't allow dating to interfere with visitation schedules or normal child–parent activities. Maintain regular one-on-one time with your child when your new partner is not part of the action. Quality time with you tells your child he is important and that you are paying attention to his needs.

— Don't allow your date or new partner to discipline your child. Your child will respond to you better than your boyfriend/girlfriend. Until the new relationship has had time to become permanent, it is better that they do not have authority over your child.

— Encourage your child to express his feelings, but do not allow him to dictate the terms of your love life. Listen to your child and validate his feelings.

— You have no obligation to let the other parent know about your casual dates. You do need to let the other parent know when you introduce your child to someone with whom you are in a more serious relationship. This is common courtesy as well as safety. All parents want to know when their children are being exposed to other adults. The other parent may not like this person, but they do need to know that they are treating your child well.

If the proper groundwork is laid, and if the new boyfriend or girlfriend is really committed to you and accepting of your child, a positive relationship can develop between your child and your new partner.

Tips for Helping Your Child Cope with Moving

Moving to a new community can be an exciting but sometimes difficult event for a child and a family. In divorced families, a move can be even more stressful if both parents are not in support of the idea. If the move becomes a source of conflict, it needs to be resolved in a way that does not drag your children into the middle. Ultimately, both of you play an important role in easing the transition for your children. Following is a guide for how parents can prepare children for a move and help them adjust to the changes:

— Timing the move is an important factor to consider. When circumstances allow for flexibility, it is better to avoid a move immediately following a divorce or midway through a school year. If there is little flexibility to time the move, the tips below will help ease the transition.

— Prepare your children by informing them early about the move. Children need time to get used to the idea. Provide age-appropriate information about the move and encourage any questions. Use storybooks to show what moving is and explain to them what will be happening. Answer questions honestly and be prepared for a variety of reactions.

— Many children will be anxious when they learn about the move because they may fear the unknown. If you are moving nearby, take your children to see the new home and neighborhood. Being able to visualize where they are going can help to relieve anxiety. If moving far away, try to gather information and images of the new destination—the town/city, house, school—to show your children. Find out what facilities and activities they can be involved in.

— Allow your children to make some choices for the new home, such as what color to paint their bedroom walls.

— Make a "packing date" where both you and your children spend time sorting and packing. Children will find it easier to do these tasks if the entire family is involved. Reward "packing dates" with pizza or movie nights.

— While packing up their things, explain what you are doing and that their toys are not being thrown out or taken away for long. It can be tempting to "clean house" and discard old toys and unused articles. But this should be done carefully; the loss of material things may overwhelm some children. Better to help them sort out the bulk of their things once they have moved to their new home and when they can feel more in control of their new environment.

— Explain to your children what will be missing in the new home, such as the couch from the living room. This will help them anticipate and adjust to the changes.

— Help your children to create an address book with contacts of friends, teachers, coaches, etc. Encourage your children to stay in touch, and assure them that their friends are just a mouse-click or postage stamp away.

— Help your children plan their goodbyes. Some may want a party while others prefer a special play date with one or two friends. Saying goodbye is an important step in the moving process.

— Together with your children, create a special box just for moving day essentials. It should include those items your children will need on the day of the move. It should also include a "Fun Bag" with some games and small toys to keep them busy on moving day. Allow your children to decorate the box.

— On moving day, put your children's furniture on the moving truck last so that it is first to unload. Try to get the children's rooms in order before the rest of the house. This will help orient them quickly to the new surroundings.

— Access religious and community organizations in your new neighborhood. They can provide a ready structure of activities, contacts, and resources for the whole family. If the family was involved with similar groups before, participating in such activities in the new location can increase feelings of familiarity.

— Encourage children to become involved in a club or sports team. This provides a ready-made group of peers on a regular basis. Parents can invite the group or team over for ice cream or pizza to help the children build new relationships. In this way parents can get to know parents of new peers.

When parents are sensitive to how moving can affect their children, they can make it a positive experience, enhancing children's emotional growth, adaptability, self-confidence, and social skills.

Attached is a copy of the chapter from today's session so you can better understand what was covered.

Upsetting Situations:
Variation for a Faraway Parent

Mom moves far away. You feel sad. You worry you won't see Mom again.

It's important for you to know: Even if Mom moves far away, she still loves you very much. You will still get to see Mom and talk to her.

Have the mom puppet say to you:
Even though I moved far away, I still love you very much.

Have the mom puppet say to you:
Even though I moved far away, we can still talk on the phone.

Have the mom puppet say to you:
Even though I moved far away, we can still see each other sometimes.

Dad moves far away. You feel sad. You worry you won't see Dad again.

It's important for you to know: Even if Dad moves far away, he still loves you very much. You will still get to see Dad and talk to him.

Have the dad puppet say to you:
Even though I moved far away, I still love you very much.

Have the dad puppet say to you:
Even though I moved far away, we can still talk on the phone.

Have the dad puppet say to you:
Even though I moved far away, we can still see each other sometimes.

Tips for Helping Children Cope with a Faraway Parent

Dear Parents,

Long-distance parenting is one of the most difficult challenges facing divorced parents and their children. It is important for both parents to work to ensure that the relationship between the parent at a distance and their child continues. This can be a challenge, particularly if there is anger or resentment about the long-distance arrangement. It requires effort and a commitment to the parent–child relationship. If both parents keep the focus on the needs of the children, it becomes easier to take the actions that will help them thrive.

Helping Your Child Cope When You Live Far Away

As the long-distance parent, you must put effort into maintaining your relationship with your child. Try to remember that being a long-distance parent does not mean that you will automatically disappear from your child's life. It just requires some motivation, creativity, and cooperation to maintain a strong relationship with your child. Below are some ideas:

— As the adult, it is your responsibility to initiate contact with your child. Do not put the onus on your child to call or email you. You take the lead! Try not to take it personally if your child does not call you right back or is not very talkative on the phone. This is pretty normal for children and usually has nothing to do with you.

— Set up a regular schedule for contact and follow it faithfully. Your child needs to be able to count on you to follow through.

— Show interest in your child's life. Ask about the things that are important to your child, such as school, friends, extra-curricular activities, etc. Know the names of your child's teacher and closest friends.

— Keep the contact with your child positive. If you feel the need to encourage improved behavior, make sure you balance those comments with positive ones. Try to give three good comments to one "do better" comment.

— When talking with your child, try to avoid asking questions that will yield yes, no, or one-word answers. Instead, ask open-ended questions that invite more. For example, instead of asking, "Did you have a good time at David's birthday party?" which will likely elicit a yes or no and then silence, ask, "What did you do at David's birthday party?" At least now, you are likely to get some information.

- Never badmouth the other parent to your child and do not use your communication time with your child to grill him about the other parent. Keep your child out of the middle.

- Send videos of yourself reading bedtime stories to your child, showing parts of your day, etc.

- Have "Show and Tell" via Skype, FaceTime, or another video-calling software. Encourage your child to show and talk about something that is important to him, such as a drawing he made.

- Create a family website and post information and pictures to each other.

- Stay in contact with your child's other parent and respect their house rules. Clear things with the other parent before mentioning them to your child.

Tips for the Residential Parent

Since your child is living with you, it becomes your responsibility to support the relationship between your child and his long-distance parent. You do not have to do all the work—just your 50%. The other 50% belongs to the long-distance parent. Below are some suggestions that will help you in your important role:

- Never badmouth the other parent to your child. What you say to your child about the other parent can influence the success or failure of your child's relationship with the long-distance parent. Remember that your child will be emotionally healthier now and in the long term if he maintains positive contact with the other parent, even if it is predominantly a long-distance relationship.

- Support the long-distance parent's attempts to stay in touch with your child. For example, ensure that your child is available for scheduled telephone calls. Or set up an email account for your child so that he can have a way to be in touch with the other parent. Give your child privacy and space to spend time with the other parent via phone, email, etc. Offer your own ideas about ways your child can maintain positive contact with the other parent.

- Share relevant information with the long-distance parent. Make it easy for the parent to get information from school, physicians, coaches, etc. Consider investing in one of the online programs that have been developed for divorced parents such as Our Family Wizard (www.ourfamilywizard.com). With it you can provide information about your child that the other parent can access day or night, and vice versa. Parents who have information tend to be more involved and feel more connected to their children.

— Help keep the other parent "alive" for your child. For instance, allow your child to display a photograph of the other parent in his bedroom. Encourage your child to talk about the other parent.

— Let your child know that you want him to spend time with his other parent. Do your part to handle travel arrangements and get your child ready to transition to the other parent.

Upsetting Situations:
Variation for an Absent Parent

You don't get to see Dad. This makes you feel very sad, angry, and confused.

It's important for you to know: Sometimes parents don't see their kids. When this happens it is because that parent has big grown-up problems that have nothing to do with anything you did wrong or bad. Even though you are not seeing Dad, you still have a mom to take care of you and love you!

Put the dad puppet on the other side of the room.

Have the mom puppet say to you:
Dad is not seeing you because he has big grown-up problems to work on.

Have the mom puppet say to you:
You did not do anything wrong or bad to make Dad go away.

Have the mom puppet say to you:
I am here to take care of you and love you.

You don't get to see Mom. This makes you feel very sad, angry, and confused.

It's important for you to know: Sometimes parents don't see their kids. When this happens it is because that parent has big grown-up problems that have nothing to do with anything you did wrong or bad. Even though you are not seeing Mom, you still have a dad to take care of you and love you!

Put the mom puppet on the other side of the room.

Have the dad puppet say to you:
Mom is not seeing you because she has big grown-up problems to work on.

Have the dad puppet say to you:
You did not do anything wrong or bad to make Mom go away.

Have the dad puppet say to you:
I am here to take care of you and love you.

Tips for Helping Your Child Cope with an Absent Parent

Dear Parent,

Your child may be estranged from a parent either because his parent abandoned the family or because access with a parent was terminated. Talking openly and appropriately with your child about the absent parent, and answering your child's questions, can ease your child's feelings of confusion, sadness, anger, guilt, and rejection. If you do not answer your child's questions, he may ask others and may not get appropriate information about his family situation. It is important that your child gets the information he needs from you. It is also better for your child to feel he can talk to you about difficult topics. Talking about your family situation with your child will help to build trust and closeness in your relationship with your child. Below are some tips for helping your child cope with an absent parent:

— Do not show your anger or frustration about the absent parent to your child, and do not badmouth the other parent, as this will only escalate your child's bad feelings. Rather, focus on your child's feelings. It is completely appropriate for you to express how disappointed you once were that the other parent was not able to be part of your family, but that is not something that should be dwelled upon in the conversations with your child.

— Talk about some of the positive things that you liked about the other parent. Do not let your negative feelings toward the other parent come out when you are having these discussions. Show your child photos of the other parent, and use these photos as a way to share appropriate information such as what their parent looked like and how you met. One idea is to put together a shoe box that contains photos, mementos, and stories of the other parent. Over the years, your child can look through the box and remember the stories connected to each item. This will help your child gain a sense of family roots and identity.

— Provide your child with information about his extended family. Again, if you have photos, this can be helpful to aid in your discussion. If not, you can draw pictures to help your child visualize his grandparents, aunts, uncles, etc.

— Young children do not need to know the details underlying the reasons for the parent's absence in their life. A general statement that alleviates potential feelings of guilt is sufficient, such as: "Mom/Dad is not seeing you because he/she has big grown-up problems. These big grown-up problems have nothing to do with anything you did wrong or bad."

— Some children need or ask for more specific information. For instance, if your child's parent has an addiction that has kept him from being an involved parent, you can say, "Your Mom is very sick. She drinks too much alcohol and that keeps her from being the type of mom who is able to live with her children." Try to tailor your words to the child's age, and do not offer more information than the child seems to be asking for, as this can cause the child to become confused or feel overwhelmed.

— If your child asks if his absent parent loves him or wonders how the absent parent may feel about him, it is best to be positive. You can say, "I'm sure if he knew you like I do he would think you are an amazing kid!" Reinforce your own love and care for your child. It can be helpful to repeat the following message often: "I love you so, so, so much and I am here to take care of you."

— Allow your child to express his own feelings such as anger, hurt, sadness, love, ambivalence, etc. Make sure that he understands that he is in no way to blame for his parent's lack of involvement. This issue may arise again and again throughout the years, especially if the other parent pops in periodically for visits and then disappears for lengthy periods. Continue to reassure your child that the other parent's decisions are not your child's fault.

There is no way to protect your child from hurt and disappointment in life. The key, though, is to keep the disappointment from being felt as a reflection of his self-worth. Helping your child cope with having an absent parent teaches him that he can deal with life's challenges. Above all, remember that you and your child are a family. Do not focus on a parent's absence or lack of involvement; rather, focus on the things that you do together, and build a solid foundation of your own.

CHAPTER OVERVIEW
When Parents Argue

Objectives
- · Verbally express feelings related to parental conflict
- · Articulate a balanced, realistic view of each parent
- · Disengage from parental conflict

Materials
- · Client's scrapbook
- · Client's Ziploc® bag
- · Tokens (or coins, carnival tickets, beads, or Lego)
- · Box filled with inexpensive prizes
- · Colored fine tip markers or colored pencils
- · Playdough
- · Three copies of "When Parents Argue" (one copy for the child's scrapbook, one copy for each parent)
- · Letter for parents (one copy for each parent)

Discussion
Conflict between parents in front of their children (especially around issues related to the children) is associated with a number of psychological problems for children, including aggression, anxiety, social skills problems, low self-esteem, and poor school performance. This chapter helps children disengage from marital conflict, which is an important psychological task for children of divorce. Once children are able to disengage from the marital conflict, they can better focus on their own lives and proceed with age-appropriate activities.

In processing this chapter, it is important not to tarnish the parents, even if children voice negative feelings toward their parents. The practitioner can highlight that everyone makes mistakes, even parents, and when parents are angry at each other, they may say or do things that they shouldn't. If parents are in therapy, it can be conveyed that they are working hard to make things better.

Another goal of this chapter is to help children express feelings regarding parental conflict. Some children may have difficulty articulating their emotional states. If this is the case, it can be helpful to refer to the Feeling Squares used in the "Feelings" chapter.

Ready-made playdough can be used, or the practitioner and child can make their own playdough. A variation to using playdough is to use marshmallow people (these can be easily made with marshmallows and pretzel sticks and the faces can be decorated with ready-to-use icing tubes). At the end of the activity, the client can eat one of the marshmallow people!

When Parents Argue

Welcome back to the story! Today we're going to talk about when parents argue. Since Cory's mom and dad do not live together anymore, they do not see each other every day. When they do see each other, sometimes they are nice to each other, and sometimes they are not nice to each other. Sometimes they look at each other in a mean way. Sometimes they say mean things to each other. Sometimes they argue with each other. Banana said, "It can be hard for kids to talk about when their parents argue. But it is important for you to talk about when Mom and Dad argue so you can let out sad, scared, upset feelings and learn ways to feel better. To make it easier for you to talk about these feelings, we're going to make playdough people, and then use the playdough people to show what happens."

You can do the playdough activity too! First, make three playdough people: Make Mom, Dad, and you.

Use the playdough people to show an argument between Mom and Dad. Show what Mom does and says when she is angry with Dad. Show what Dad does and says when he is angry with Mom.

Next, answer the questions below:

What do Mom and Dad argue about?

When Mom is angry with Dad, what does she say to him? (Show with the playdough people.)

When Dad is angry with Mom, what does he say to her? (Show with the playdough people.)

When Mom and Dad argue, how do you feel?

When Mom and Dad argue, what do you do? (Show with the playdough people.)

Sometimes Mom and Dad argue about Cory. This makes Cory feel bad. Banana said, "Cory, when parents argue, it can make kids feel like they did something wrong or bad. When Mom and Dad argue, it is important for you to know that it is a problem between them, and it is not your fault. Even if Mom and Dad are arguing about you, it is still not your fault." Hearing this helped Cory feel better!

Does Cory feel better knowing that when Mom and Dad argue, it is not Cory's fault?

When Mom and Dad argue, it is a problem between them, and it is not your fault. Make the mom and dad playdough people say to you, "When we argue, it's not your fault!"

When Mom and Dad argue, Cory feels scared. When Mom and Dad argue, Cory sometimes gets a tummy ache. Banana said, "Cory, when parents argue, it can make kids feel scared and upset. When Mom and Dad argue, it is important for you to know that they still love you. Even if Mom and Dad are arguing about you, they still love you, no matter what!"

How does Cory feel when Mom and Dad argue?

How do you feel when your mom and dad argue?

Even when Mom and Dad argue, they still love you, no matter what. Make the mom and dad playdough people say to you, "We still love you, no matter what!"

Cory wants Mom and Dad to stop arguing. Cory wants Mom and Dad to be nice to each other. Banana explained, "Cory, I know you want Mom and Dad to stop arguing. You may even try to make them stop but they don't listen. They keep arguing. Sometimes it's really hard for parents to learn nice ways to talk to each other. It is very important for you to know that it is not your job to make Mom and Dad stop arguing. And remember what I said before...even when Mom and Dad argue, they still love you, no matter what!" Hearing this again helped Cory feel better.

It is not up to kids to make their parents stop arguing. Make the mom and dad playdough people say to you, "It is not your job to make us stop arguing."

Even though Cory feels sad and scared when Mom and Dad argue, does it help to know that Mom and Dad love Cory, no matter what?

Banana said, "When your parents argue, you can say to yourself (not out loud) 'Mom and Dad love me, no matter what.' This can help you feel better." Cory wanted to feel better. So Cory decided when Mom and Dad argue to say (not out loud), "Mom and Dad still love me, no matter what!"

You can also help yourself feel better when your mom and dad argue. Use the playdough people to show an argument between Mom and Dad. While the playdough mom and dad are arguing, say to yourself (not out loud), "Mom and Dad love me, no matter what!"

What can you do to help yourself feel better from now on when Mom and Dad argue?

Dear Parents,

It is normal to feel angry, frustrated, and resentful toward the other parent. However, how you express these negative feelings, particularly in the presence of your child, can significantly impair your child's healthy functioning. Conflict between parents in front of children (especially around issues related to the children) is associated with a number of psychological problems for children, including aggression, anxiety, social skills problems, low self-esteem, and poor school performance. When parents argue or fight in front of their children, they teach their children that conflict is resolved by being verbally or physically aggressive. When parents argue or fight in front of their children, it heightens children's fears. It makes them worry, for example, "Are my parents fighting because of me?" "What's wrong with me that I can't stop the fighting?" "Will I not get to see my parent anymore?" "Will my parents hurt each other?"

One of the most important ways **you can help** your child is by avoiding conflict with the other parent in your child's presence. This includes avoiding conflict during times both parents and the children are physically together, as well as during phone conversations when children are exposed to one end of the conversation. You should assume that if your child is in the home, he can overhear the phone conversation, even if he is in another room or you think he is asleep. In the book *Making Divorce Easier on Your Child*, authors Long and Forehand recommend the following:

—   Do not argue in front of your child. If the other parent tries to start an argument, say firmly and politely, "Let's arrange another time to discuss that matter." If necessary, turn and walk away. Schedule a time to discuss the issues with the other parent when the child is not present or nearby.

—   When you do discuss issues with the other parent, without the child being present, adhere to these rules: (1) Focus on what is best for your child. (2) Remain calm and be respectful, no matter how angry or verbally aggressive the other parent becomes. (3) Focus on the issue of concern, and avoid bringing up other issues or the other parent's faults. (4) Use problem-solving principles such as defining the problem, brainstorming appropriate solutions, evaluating possible solutions, deciding which solution to use, and evaluating how well it worked. Additional tips for negotiating with the other parent can be found in the book *Smart Parenting During and After Divorce* by Peter Favaro.

—   If an argument with the other parent does occur in front of your child, do not talk about the issue with your child until you are calm. Then in your conversation with your child, do not put all the blame on the other parent. It takes two to have a conflict! Tell your child that you are sorry he heard the arguing. Explain that the two of you did not agree and that you are going to do everything you can to work out an appropriate solution. Reassure your child that the disagreement is not his fault. And most importantly, say to your child, "Even when we argue, we still love you, no matter what!"

— Recognize when you need help from a third party such as a mediator, parenting coordinator, or attorney.

Attached is a copy of the chapter from today's session so you can better understand what was covered.

CHAPTER OVERVIEW
Wishing Mom and Dad Will Live Together Again

Objectives
- Normalize reunification fantasies
- Accept the finality of the divorce

Materials
- Client's scrapbook
- Client's Ziploc® bag
- Tokens (or coins, carnival tickets, beads, or Lego)
- Box filled with inexpensive prizes
- Colored fine tip markers or colored pencils
- Magic carpet (i.e., a large towel or blanket)
- Paper and coloring supplies
- Three copies of "Wishing Mom and Dad Will Live Together Again" (one copy for the child's scrapbook, one copy for each parent)
- Letter for parents (one copy for each parent)

Discussion
It is common for children of divorce, particularly young children, to fantasize about their parents getting back together. Part of the reason for this is the young child's limited understanding of relationships and his rich imagination and fantasy life. This may also be a coping strategy for children to avoid painful feelings and attempts to maintain life as they know it. Alternatively, one parent does not want the divorce and enlists the child in convincing the other parent to stay married. This can have a negative impact on children as it can lead to increased feelings of insecurity and an exaggerated sense of personal power. An important psychological task is for children to accept the permanence of the divorce, so they do not remain stuck trying to get their parents back together. This chapter facilitates this task.

A script is provided for the magic carpet ride, but it can be modified—creativity and an enthusiastic, animated tone is encouraged!

The letter for parents highlights the important role parents play in helping their children to adjust to the reality of the finality of divorce.

Wishing Mom and Dad Will Live Together Again

Welcome back to the story! Today we're going to talk about wishes. Banana said, "Cory, sometimes kids wish for things that might come true, and sometimes kids wish for things that cannot come true. Today we're going to talk about different kinds of wishes. To help us do that, we're going to go on a pretend magic carpet ride!" Wow, what fun, thought Cory!

You and your therapist can go on a pretend magic carpet ride too! Hop on the special carpet. Pretend that it is a magic carpet! Your therapist will sit on the magic carpet too. Listen carefully as your therapist reads the script for your magic carpet ride.

Script for Magic Carpet Ride

This carpet is magic because it can fly. It's moving! We're flying up into the sky! Wheeee! We're flying through the air! What fun! Now the magic carpet is resting on a soft, cushy cloud. (Feel the soft, fluffy white cloud.) Look down there. (Point to a distant spot.) I can see my house and the park. And look at all those cars! What do you see down there? (Allow client to answer.)

We're moving again. We're gently flying through the air. Hey, look at that flock of birds—we're flying as fast as them! (Wave to the birds.) Now we're flying down. Whoosh! We're landing! (Bump to a landing.) Now we're in The Land Where All Wishes Come True! Wow, look at this magical place! See the purple grass and the sparkly trees and the colorful rainbow and the butterflies made out of gold? It's so amazing!

In this very special land all wishes come true, even super-duper crazy wishes come true! I wish for candy to fall from the sky! Poof! My wish came true! Look at all this candy… Giant lollipops! Gummy bears! Caramels! Jelly beans! Now it's your turn to make a wish. What do you wish for? (Allow client to answer.) This land where all wishes come true is so cool! I feel so happy here!

Uh, oh! We're moving again… We're going up! Whoosh! We're way up in the sky! We're gently gliding along. Feel the cool air on our face. Look over there, an airplane! (Wave to the people on the plane.) We're moving down, we're landing. Looks like we're back home. (Bump to a landing and get off.) We're back in my therapy room. (Point out some things you see in the room.)

Banana said, "That magic carpet ride was pretty cool! It would be so wonderful if all our wishes came true, for real! But we were just pretending. In real life, all our wishes cannot come true. And that can make us feel sad and disappointed. Like, I wish it could be my birthday every day so I could get lots of presents! Even if I wish really hard, I cannot make this wish come true. Lots of kids whose parents are divorced wish their mom and dad would live happily together again. But when parents divorce, it's usually forever. Even if we wish really hard, sometimes our wishes cannot come true." Cory knew Banana was right. Cory knew Mom and Dad would probably never live happily together again. This made Cory feel sad.

Do lots of kids whose parents are divorced wish their mom and dad would live happily together again?

When parents divorce, is it usually forever?

How does Cory feel knowing Mom and Dad will probably never live happily together again?

How do you feel knowing your mom and dad will probably never live happily together again?

All of a sudden, Cory thought of something. Cory said, "I've seen lots of movies. And in the movies, wishes come true. So maybe if I wish really, really hard, my wish will come true. Mom and Dad will live happily together again." Banana replied, "Cory, it's different in the movies. Movies are not real. Movies are just pretend. So even if you wish really, really hard, Mom and Dad will probably never live happily together again. But instead of feeling sad that your mom and dad will probably never live happily together again, you can think of something happy, and this can help you feel better. What is something you can think of that makes you feel happy?" Cory thought for a moment, then said, "I feel happy when I think of playing at the park."

Banana said, "When you feel sad about your mom and dad's divorce, you can think of playing at the park, and this can help you feel better."

If Cory wishes really, really hard, will Mom and Dad live happily together again?

If you wish really, really hard, will your Mom and Dad live happily together again?

If Cory thinks of something happy, can this help Cory feel better?

What makes Cory feel happy?

What makes you feel happy?

Pretend you are feeling sad. Then think of something that makes you feel happy. Show how you can help yourself feel better by thinking of something that makes you feel happy.

Draw a picture of something that makes you feel happy. When you feel sad, you can think of what makes you feel happy, and this can help you feel better.

Dear Parents,

Children in divorced families often hope their parents will reunite. In fact, many children harbor a fantasy about reunification that lasts for years. Children may act out, so their parents have to work together to address their behavior problems. This can be an attempt to reunite their parents. Reunification fantasies can have a negative impact on children as it can lead to increased feelings of insecurity and an exaggerated sense of personal power. When children remain stuck trying to get their parents back together, it can interfere with their healthy functioning.

You play an important role in helping your child accept the fact that your divorce is final. **You can help** by giving your child a clear explanation that reuniting is not going to happen. For example, say, "We know you would really like it if we would stay married and live happily together again. But we cannot live happily together again. We have made the decision to divorce, and this decision is final. We will never get back together. This is a decision that is up to a mom and a dad. It is not a kid decision. This means you cannot change our decision to stay divorced. I know this is very hard for you. Let's talk about how you're feeling right now."

It may be difficult for you to talk to your children about the divorce in such a direct manner and to end your children's wishes to reunite your family. It can be helpful to prepare for this discussion by anticipating the feelings you might experience, such as sadness or guilt. If you are able to manage your own feelings, you will be able to better respond to your child's feelings and reactions. Even though conversations like these can be difficult, know that you and your child will adjust better in the long run if these issues are addressed appropriately.

If one of you does not want the divorce, you need to deal with your feelings of grief with the help of a supportive adult so you and your child can move forward and adapt to your new life circumstances.

You can help by providing your child with a more cooperative parental relationship and reduce conflict in front of your child. This will in turn provide your child more security and an appreciation that good things can come out of the divorce too. This helps children accept the finality of divorce more readily.

Attached is a copy of the chapter from today's session so you can better understand what was covered.

CHAPTER OVERVIEW
Forever Love

Objectives
- Verbalize an understanding that love between parents and their children never ends
- Verbalize an understanding that parents love their children unconditionally

Materials
- Client's scrapbook
- Client's Ziploc® bag
- Tokens (or coins, carnival tickets, beads, or Lego)
- Box filled with inexpensive prizes
- Colored fine tip markers or colored pencils
- Colored markers and paper
- Photo of the client and his parents (or child can draw a picture)
- Three copies of "Forever Love" (one copy for the child's scrapbook, one copy for each parent)
- Letter for parents (one copy for each parent)

Discussion
Children often have a difficult time understanding that the love between parents and the love between parents and their children is different. Children need a direct explanation and repeated reassurance that the love between parents and their children never ends. While this chapter explains to children the concept of forever love, it is ultimately up to the parents to help their children feel loved unconditionally. Some parents need guidance on how to communicate their unconditional love to their child, and how to genuinely support the other parent's loving relationship. In addition to the letter for parents, conjoint sessions can be helpful in strengthening the parent–child bond.

Forever Love

Welcome back to the story! Today we're going to talk about forever love. Cory knew that Mom and Dad got a divorce because they stopped being happy together. Cory knew that Mom and Dad got a divorce because they stopped loving each other. Cory said to Banana, "I have a worry. If Mom and Dad got a divorce because they stopped loving each other, I have a worry that Mom and Dad will stop loving me too." Banana said, "Cory, lots of kids whose parents are divorced worry that their parents will stop loving them like they stopped loving each other. But love between parents is different than love between parents and their kids. Love between parents and kids is a special kind of love. Love between parents and kids is forever love. This means that your mom and dad will love you forever, no matter what!" Hearing this helped Cory feel better!

Is love between parents and kids forever love?

Will your mom and dad love you forever, no matter what?

Banana explained, "We're going to play a game to help us learn that parents love their kids forever, no matter what. It's called the Forever Love game. Let's follow the instructions to learn how to play." Cory was excited to play the game!

You can play the game too. Follow the instructions below to play the game.

Forever Love

Step 1: Draw a picture of a sad face (you can draw it on your own or ask your therapist to help). Then, on the other side of the paper, draw a picture of a heart (you can draw it on your own or ask your therapist to help).

Step 2: Your therapist will read some questions. You have to answer the question by holding up the sad face or the heart. Here is an example:

Question:

You come into your house with muddy shoes and you get mud all over the carpet. This makes Dad very angry at you. Does this mean that Dad doesn't love you anymore?

(If you think the answer is: Dad doesn't love me anymore, then hold up the sad face. If you think the answer is: Dad will love me, no matter what, then hold up the heart.)

In this example, the right answer is for you to hold up the heart because parents love their kids forever, no matter what!

Now it's your turn to play the game.

Question:

You are playing ball in the house and you knock over the lamp and it breaks. This makes Dad very angry at you. Does this mean that Dad doesn't love you anymore?

(If you think the answer is: Dad doesn't love me anymore, then hold up the sad face. If you think the answer is: Dad will love me, no matter what, then hold up the heart.)

Question:

You're supposed to spend the day with Mom but Dad calls to say he got tickets to take you to the baseball game. You tell Mom you would rather go with Dad to the baseball game. This makes Mom feel sad. Does this mean that Mom doesn't love you anymore?

(If you think the answer is: Mom doesn't love me anymore, then hold up the sad face. If you think the answer is: Mom will love me, no matter what, then hold up the heart.)

Question:

Mom won't let you stay up late to watch a television program so you yell at Mom, "I hate you!" This makes Mom feel sad and angry. Does this mean that Mom doesn't love you anymore?

(If you think the answer is: Mom doesn't love me anymore, then hold up the sad face. If you think the answer is: Mom will love me, no matter what, then hold up the heart.)

Question:

Dad is supposed to take you to the zoo but he calls to say he can't take you because he has to go to work. Does this mean that Dad doesn't love you anymore?

(If you think the answer is: Dad doesn't love me anymore, then hold up the sad face. If you think the answer is: Dad will love me, no matter what, then hold up the heart.)

After they played the Forever Love game, Banana said, "The right answer for all the questions was to hold up the heart. Do you know why?" Cory answered, "Because parents love their kids forever, no matter what!" "That's exactly right! No matter what happens, parents always love their kids. Even when your parents are mad at you, and even when you don't always want to be with your parent, and even when you're mad at your parents, and even when your parent misses a visit, parents still love their kids, no matter what!" Cory's face had a big smile because Cory felt happy knowing that love between parents and their kids is forever love.

The right answer for all the questions was to hold up the heart. How come?

How come Cory's face had a big smile?

Show with your face how you feel knowing that love between parents and their kids is forever love.

Your mom and dad both love you very, very much. Your mom and dad love you forever! Draw a heart (you can draw it on your own or ask your therapist to help). Inside the heart, draw a picture of you and your mom and dad. Let this be a reminder that your mom and dad love you forever!

Dear Parents,

Although the love between you and the other parent ends, the love between you and your child does not. This is obvious to a loving parent. Children, however, often have a difficult time understanding that the love between parents and the love between parents and their children is different. Children need a direct explanation and repeated reassurance that the love between parents and their children never ends. **You can help** by telling your child often how much you love him. When your child has done something wrong or bad, or when there has been a disagreement between you and your child, it is even more important to reassure your child of your love for him.

There are many creative ways to convey your love for your child. Below are some ideas from the book *101 Ways to Tell Your Child I Love You* by Vicky Lansky:

1. Have a secret I LOVE YOU signal, i.e., touch your nose and then your child's.

2. Learn to say I LOVE YOU in sign language.

3. Kiss the palm of your child's hand then close the hand to "hold" the kiss for later use, in times of need.

4. Mail an I LOVE YOU letter or card to your child.

5. Write a letter to your child about the special day he was born (be sure to include how happy you and the other parent were on the day).

6. Ask your child to pick a number from one to ten then deliver that many kisses.

7. Play the "I love you more than..." game, i.e., "I love you more than all the stars in the sky" or "all the ice cream in the world."

8. Put your ear to your child's belly button and say, "I am listening to a little voice inside your tummy and I hear a request for a hug."

9. Cut out two paper hearts and place them on your child's pillow, and say, "Mom and Dad love you forever!"

10. After disciplining your child, say, "I may not always love your behavior but I always love you!"

Buying your child lavish gifts, or trying to "outdo" the other parent, is not an appropriate way to show love to your child. Rather, spending consistent quality time with your child and expressing your unconditional love are what your child needs from you.

Attached is a copy of the chapter from today's session so you can better understand what was covered.

CHAPTER OVERVIEW
Reviewing What Was Learned
(***Note: This overview is for the next two chapters)

Objectives
- Articulate an appropriate understanding of why therapy is ending
- Review and celebrate therapeutic gains
- Receive a concrete reminder of the therapeutic experience upon termination
- Experience a positive termination from therapy

Materials (For the Last Two Sessions)
- Client's scrapbook
- Client's Ziploc® bag
- Tokens (or coins, carnival tickets, beads, or Lego)
- Box filled with inexpensive prizes
- Colored fine tip markers or colored pencils
- Paper
- Masking tape (optional)
- Question Cards (included)
- Small gift box
- Wrapping paper (three different kinds) or tissue paper (three different colors)
- Tape
- Gift (See Discussion section below)
- Three copies of "Reviewing What Was Learned" (one copy for the child's scrapbook, one copy for each parent)
- Three copies of "The Last Day of Therapy" (one copy for the child's scrapbook, one copy for each parent)
- Letter from the Therapist (See Discussion section below)
- Letter from the Parents (See Discussion section below)
- Letter for parents (one copy for each parent)

Discussion
Children of divorce have a history of prior losses and difficult goodbyes. Termination with these children, therefore, provides a unique opportunity for the practitioner to provide the client with a new experience of loss; one that the client is appropriately prepared for and one that is embedded with positive messages.

This chapter and the next are intended for the client's last two sessions of therapy. The goals are to review what the client has learned over the course of treatment, prepare the client for termination, process the client's feelings about ending therapy, and provide a positive goodbye experience. (While the focus of the last two sessions is on termination, it is best practice to raise the topic of termination with the parents and child well in advance of the last two sessions.)

The Crumpled Paper Throw game is a fun and active intervention to help the client consolidate therapeutic gains. Prior to playing the game, the practitioner can place masking tape on the floor to create a "throw" line. The practitioner should stand far enough from the "throw" line to make the game challenging, and at the same time, to ensure the client can have some success in throwing the crumpled paper through the hoop. During game play, the practitioner cheers the client on and offers praise for correct responses to the questions.

The client's last session should be carefully planned and, ideally, involve both parents. The chapter will need to be modified if the parents are not willing to participate together, or if the practitioner feels that the tension between the parents would create a negative atmosphere for the child and it would be better to conduct the session with the child and each parent separately.

The practitioner can write a letter to read to the child at the last session (see the Sample Letter from the Therapist in Appendix C). The practitioner can modify the letter so that it is tailored to the client, reviews goals achieved in therapy, and provides healing messages. The letter can be placed on the last page of the child's scrapbook.

The practitioner can meet with the parents in advance of the last session to enlist their involvement and prepare them. Parents can be coached to write a letter to their child that they can read in the last session. These letters can also go in the child's scrapbook.

The child is given the scrapbook in the last session. Prior to the last session, the practitioner can discuss with the parents where in the child's home the scrapbook will be kept to ensure its privacy and safekeeping. (Hopefully, the parents can agree on one home for the scrapbook! If not, they can make a copy and keep one in each home.) A complete copy of the scrapbook must be made for the practitioner's file prior to giving it to the client. The child will have an opportunity to share parts of the scrapbook with his parents in the last session. The practitioner can prepare the parents for this and offer them appropriate ways to respond to the content.

A gift-giving activity is incorporated into the last session. The practitioner can be creative in giving a gift that is therapeutic. The gift can be one item (or several small items) placed in a box along with an accompanying message identifying something special about the gift. Below are some suggestions:

A balloon to celebrate all your hard work.

A happy face sticker because talking about your feelings can help you feel better.

A cookie so you remember to do Cookie Breathing to help you feel better.

Bubbles to pop your worries away.

Glitter hearts to show that your mom and dad love you forever, no matter what!

Ten tokens so you can pick a prize from my special box one last time.

The box containing the gift or gifts should be wrapped in three layers of different types of wrapping paper or different color of tissue paper, and each time the child answers one of the three questions, he can unwrap one layer of the gift. Once the child has answered the third question, he can unwrap the last layer to get the gift.

Termination from therapy can be a difficult time for the client. The client's potential feelings of anger, hurt, rejection, and abandonment are minimized by providing a positive end to therapy. The scrapbook and the gift become transitional objects for the client, as they are positive reminders of his experience and a permanent connection to therapy. Moreover, the healing messages from the therapist's letter and from the gift card provide a reminder that the client is cared for, which strengthens his self-worth.

Reviewing What Was Learned

Welcome back to the story! Today we're going to talk about all the important things that were learned in therapy. Banana said, "Cory, you learned a lot of important things in here. You learned about divorce. You learned about feelings. You learned ways to feel better. Today we're going to play a game to help us talk about the important things you learned in therapy. It's called Crumpled Paper Throw game. Let's follow the instructions below to play the game."

You can play the game too. Follow the instructions below to set up and play the game with your therapist.

Crumpled Paper Throw
Crumple a piece of paper into a ball and toss the paper ball into the circle hoop your therapist makes with her arms. Throw the crumpled paper toward the circle hoop. If you get the crumpled paper through the hoop, you earn two points. If you miss, answer one of the questions below. (Your therapist will read each question to you.) Once you have answered the question you get one point. At the end of the game, trade in points for prizes: 1–10 points = 1 prize, 11 or more points = 2 prizes.

What is divorce?

How come your mom and dad got a divorce?

Did you do anything wrong or bad to make your mom and dad get a divorce?

Even when your mom and dad argue, do they still love you, no matter what?

Is love between parents and their children the kind of love that is forever?

When you are upset, what can you do to feel better?

Banana said, "Cory, you worked hard in therapy and you learned a lot—I am very proud of you! You are ready to stop coming to therapy because you got the help you needed. As we talked about before, next time you come here will be your last time coming. Your parents will come with you to help make it special. We will do some special activities and then we will say goodbye to each other for the last time. How do you feel that next time is your last time coming here?" Cory answered, "I feel happy and sad. I feel happy because I got help from you and I feel much better now. But I feel sad because I like coming here and I will miss you." Banana said, "I enjoy being with you and I will miss you too. Sometimes it's hard to say goodbye to someone that you won't see again. But you can feel good knowing when we say goodbye it's because you are ready to stop coming here. You can feel good knowing you worked hard in here and got the help you needed!"

How come Cory is ready to stop coming to therapy?

How come you are ready to stop coming to therapy?

Cory feels happy and sad knowing next time will be the last time coming to therapy. How do you feel knowing next time will be your last time coming here?

You will get to take your scrapbook home next time you come here. You will get to show your scrapbook to your parents. Pick one of your favorite pages from your scrapbook to show your parents next time you come here.

Dear Parents,

The last phase of your child's therapy is a time to review goals achieved, process feelings about ending treatment, and prepare for a positive termination from therapy. Your involvement in the last session will help make it special. **You can help** by writing a letter to your child that you will read to him in the last session. The letter will then be placed in your child's scrapbook. Here are some suggestions of what to include in the letter to your child. This is just a guideline—feel free to change the wording and include other things that will be meaningful for your child:

- **Comment on the progress your child has made in therapy.** Be as specific as possible. For example:

> *When you started therapy, it was hard for you to talk about your feelings. Now we have lots of talks about your feelings. You are able to tell me when you feel sad or angry. And you learned to do Cookie Breathing to help yourself feel better. I am proud of you and all the new things you learned to do!*

- **Reassure your child**: Divorce is stressful for everyone in the family, especially for kids. You can help your child by giving them reassuring messages such as:

> *I know things have been hard for you since we got a divorce. But always remember that you have a mom and a dad who both love you very much.*

> *I know it upsets you when we argue in front of you or say mean things to each other. We will try our very, very best to be nice and respectful to each other.*

- **End with a loving message:** Although you probably tell your child over and over that you love him, it is still important to include a loving message at the end of your letter. Write whatever comes from your heart!

Please bring two copies of the letter—one to put in your child's scrapbook, and one for my file.

We will devote time in the last session to look at parts of your child's scrapbook. Your positive and validating response to seeing the scrapbook will help make the sharing of it meaningful to your child. Helpful statements include, "You're excited to show me one of your favorite parts of your scrapbook!" and "I can see that you feel proud of the important activities you did in therapy. I feel proud of you too!" These supportive messages will help your child feel good about sharing the scrapbook with you.

Your child will be given his scrapbook to take home in the last session. It is important for the scrapbook to be kept in a safe, private place. It can be helpful for your child to look through the scrapbook every so often as a way to reinforce key concepts learned in therapy.

You have also made significant gains in therapy. For example, you have learned ways to help your child appropriately express and manage emotions; strategies for easing your child's stress of transitioning between homes; the importance of supporting your child's positive relationship with the other parent; and tips for avoiding conflict with the other parent in your child's presence. Although the end of therapy does not mean that all your problems have been fixed, you can certainly feel good about all the goals you and your child have achieved.

The divorce will have a different meaning to your child as he matures, which can impair his healthy development. Therefore, your child may benefit from periodic therapy sessions in the future. It is recommended to schedule "booster" sessions from time to time to provide your child with ongoing support and intervention. This is something we can discuss further so we can come up with a plan that makes sense for your family.

Attached is a copy of the chapter from today's session so you can better understand what was covered.

The Last Day of Therapy

Welcome back to the story! Today is a special day. Today is Cory's last day of therapy. Cory's mom and dad came with Cory to the last day of therapy. Banana said, "Cory, it looks like you brought some important people with you today—your parents are here! Your parents came to help make today extra special. I have some special things planned for your last time here. First, your parents are going to read a letter they each wrote to you, then I am going to read a letter I wrote to you."

Your parents and your therapist wrote letters to you too. Listen carefully as they read their letters.

Cory liked the letters from Mom, Dad, and Banana. Their letters made Cory feel special. Their letters made Cory feel happy. Banana said, "Cory, we're going to put the letters in your scrapbook. Your scrapbook has all the important activities you did in therapy. You get to take your scrapbook home today. You can look at your scrapbook every once in a while as a reminder of all the important things you learned in therapy. You get to show your parents one of your favorite pages from your scrapbook."

Your scrapbook is filled with all the hard work you did in therapy. Show your parents one of your favorite pages from your scrapbook. Tell why it's one of your favorites.

Banana said, "I have a small present for you. It's wrapped in three different layers of wrapping paper. Each time you answer one of the three questions, you get to unwrap a different layer of the present. Answer all three questions to get the present!" Cory was excited to get a present from Banana.

Your therapist has a present for you too! Each time you answer one of the questions below, you get to unwrap a layer of the present. Answer all three questions to get the present!

Question #1:

You did lots of activities in therapy. Which activity did you like best? (After you answer this question, unwrap a layer of the present.)

Question #2:

You learned to do Cookie Breathing to help you feel better when you are scared or upset. Do it now to show how good you are at it! (After you show Cookie Breathing, unwrap a layer of the present.)

Question #3:

You learned a lot of important things in therapy. One of the things you learned is that your parents love you forever, no matter what! Point to the two people in the room who love you forever, no matter what! (After you do this, unwrap the last layer to get your present!)

Cory was excited to get a present from Banana. After Cory opened the present, Banana said, "Cory, now it's time to say goodbye to each other. I feel a little sad because I will miss you. But mostly I feel happy because you are leaving here with your scrapbook, a present, and two parents who love you forever, no matter what!

Appendix A

PARENT QUESTIONNAIRE

Child's Name: _____ Date of Birth: _____

Mother's Name: _____ Date of Birth: _____

Mother's Address: _____

Mother's Home Phone #: _____ Mother's Work #: _____ Mother's Cell #: _____

Mother's Educational Background, Occupation: _____

Father's Name: _____ Date of Birth: _____

Father's Address: _____

Father's Home Phone #: _____ Father's Work #: _____ Father's Cell #: _____

Father's Educational Background, Occupation: _____

Child's School: _____ Teacher: _____ Grade: _____ Phone #: _____

Who has legal custody of the child? _____ (Provide copy of custody order for the file)

List all those living in your child's home:

Name	Relationship	Age/School/Occupation

List other persons closely involved with your child but not living in the home:

_____

_____

_____

What are your concerns about your child that made you bring him/her to therapy?

_____

_____

_____

List any complications at birth and delays in development or difficulties when your child was an infant/toddler:

_____

_____

_____

_____

List any ongoing health concerns/allergies/medications your child is taking and describe for what purpose:

_____

_____

_____

_____

Describe any serious difficulties or life stresses your child has experienced, other than the separation/divorce:

_____

_____

_____

_____

Describe prior assessment/therapy your child received (name of professional, dates of service, diagnosis, nature of interventions):

_____

_____

_____

_____

Describe any concerns raised by daycare/school about your child (behavioral, peer, academic):

_____

_____

_____

_____

Describe your relationship with your child's other parent prior to separation (when and how you met, length of courtship, date of marriage, positive and negative aspects of your relationship):

_____

_____

_____

_____

Explain the circumstances of the marital separation (date of separation, who initiated and why):

_____

_____

_____

_____

What is the current legal status? (Custody, visitation arrangements, upcoming court dates):

_____

_____

_____

_____

When and how did you explain the reason for the separation to your child?

_____

_____

_____

_____

Describe your child's reaction to the marital separation immediately afterward and since the separation:

_____

_____

_____

_____

What is the most difficult question your child has asked about the divorce, and how did you respond?

_____

_____

_____

_____

Describe any ongoing conflicts between you and the other parent (give examples of the conflicts and how conflicts are generally managed):

_____

_____

_____

_____

Give examples of ways you have cooperated well with the other parent:

_____

_____

_____

_____

Give examples of ways you have reassured your child/tried to improve life for your child:

_____

_____

_____

_____

Are you or the other parent presently dating? Please elaborate and describe your child's reaction:

_____

_____

_____

_____

Have there been any other major changes in the home situation, i.e., have you moved, has your work schedule changed, etc.?

_____

_____

_____

_____

Describe your relationship with your child, and your strengths and weaknesses as a parent:

_____

_____

_____

_____

What role do you see the other parent playing in your child's life?

_____

_____

_____

_____

List any books on divorce you have read or your child has read:

_____

_____

_____

_____

On a scale of 1–10 (1= not coping well and 10 = coping well), how do you think you are coping with the divorce? Please elaborate:

_____

_____

_____

_____

Describe any concerns about your family (health, mental illness, alcohol/drug dependency, abuse):

_____

_____

_____

_____

Please describe any concerns about your child listed below:

Difficulty sleeping/frequent nightmares _____

Bed-wetting or soiling: _____

Unusually clingy or immature behavior: _____

Excessive fears, anxiety: _____

Physical complaints (stomachaches, headaches): _____

Change in eating habits: _____

Little sense of joy/happiness: _____

Hurts self on purpose/talks of wanting to die: _____

Blatant misbehavior: _____

Aggressive with others: _____

Hurts animals on purpose: _____

Sets fires: _____

Lies/steals: _____

Hides food: _____

School difficulties: _____

Difficulties with peers: _____

Inappropriate sexual behavior: _____

Poor self-esteem: _____

Please describe any other concerns you have about your child:

_____

_____

_____

_____

_____

What are your child's strengths, interests, and involvement in extra-curricular activities?

_____

_____

_____

_____

Mother's Background:

Where were you raised and by whom? Describe past/current relationship with your parents:

_____

_____

_____

_____

_____

List brothers and sisters, their ages, whereabouts, current relationship you have with them:

_____

_____

_____

_____

_____

Describe any of the following you/your family experienced during childhood and how it affected you: physical/sexual abuse, neglect, abandonment, spousal abuse, divorce, other trauma. (**Note:** If you have information to share that you would prefer to discuss when we meet face to face, it's okay to just put: _To be discussed when we meet._)

_____

_____

_____

_____

_____

_____

_____

_____

_____

_____

_____

_____

Describe the happiest time/experience you recall from your childhood:

_____

_____

_____

_____

Describe the saddest time/experience you recall from your childhood:

_____

_____

_____

_____

_____

Describe if you or any relatives have ever had any of the following:

Serious illness: _____

Depression/bipolar disorder: _____

Anxiety disorder: _____

Obsessive-compulsive disorder: _____

Learning disability/ADHD: _____

Eating disorder: _____

Alcoholism/drug abuse: _____

Criminal conviction: _____

Have you been seen previously for assessment/counseling/marital counseling/parenting coordination or are you currently in therapy? (If yes, indicate name of professional, date/place of service, for what purpose, and any diagnosis provided.)

_____

_____

_____

_____

_____

Please add any other information about your background that you feel is relevant:

_____

_____

_____

_____

_____

_____

_____

_____

_____

_____

_____

_____

_____

_____

_____

_____

_____

_____

_____

_____

_____

_____

_____

_____

_____

_____

_____

_____

_____

_____

Father's Background:

Where were you raised and by whom? Describe past/current relationship with your parents:

_____

_____

_____

_____

_____

List brothers and sisters, their ages, whereabouts, current relationship you have with them:

_____

_____

_____

_____

Describe any of the following you/your family experienced during childhood and how it affected you: physical/sexual abuse, neglect, abandonment, spousal abuse, divorce, other trauma. (**Note:** If you have information to share that you would prefer to discuss when we meet face to face, it's okay to just put: *To be discussed when we meet*.)

_____

_____

_____

_____

_____

_____

_____

_____

_____

_____

_____

_____

Describe the happiest time/experience you recall from your childhood:

_____

_____

_____

_____

Describe the saddest time/experience you recall from your childhood:

_____

_____

_____

_____

_____

Describe if you or any relatives have ever had any of the following:

Serious illness: _____

Depression/bipolar disorder: _____

Anxiety disorder: _____

Obsessive-compulsive disorder: _____

Learning disability/ADHD: _____

Eating disorder: _____

Alcoholism/drug abuse: _____

Criminal conviction: _____

Have you been seen previously for assessment/counseling/marital counseling/parenting coordination or are you currently in therapy? (If yes, indicate name of professional, date/place of service, for what purpose, and any diagnosis provided.)

_____

_____

_____

_____

_____

Please add any other information about your background that you feel is relevant:

_____
_____
_____
_____
_____
_____
_____
_____
_____
_____
_____
_____
_____
_____
_____
_____
_____
_____
_____
_____
_____
_____
_____
_____
_____
_____

Background of Other Primary Caregivers (i.e., Stepparent, Common Law Partner):

Where were you raised and by whom? Describe past/current relationship with your parents:

_____

_____

_____

_____

_____

List brothers and sisters, their ages, whereabouts, current relationship you have with them:

_____

_____

_____

_____

_____

Describe any of the following you/your family experienced during childhood and how it affected you: physical/sexual abuse, neglect, abandonment, spousal abuse, divorce, other trauma. (**Note:** If you have information to share that you would prefer to discuss when we meet face to face, it's okay to just put: *To be discussed when we meet*.)

_____

_____

_____

_____

_____

_____

_____

_____

_____

_____

_____

_____

Describe the happiest time/experience you recall from your childhood:

_____

_____

_____

_____

Describe the saddest time/experience you recall from your childhood:

_____

_____

_____

_____

_____

Describe if you or any relatives have ever had any of the following:

Serious illness: _____

Depression/bipolar disorder: _____

Anxiety disorder: _____

Obsessive-compulsive disorder: _____

Learning disability/ADHD: _____

Eating disorder: _____

Alcoholism/drug abuse: _____

Criminal conviction: _____

Have you been seen previously for assessment/counseling/marital counseling/parenting coordination or are you currently in therapy? (If yes, indicate name of professional, date/place of service, for what purpose, and any diagnosis provided.)

_____

_____

_____

_____

_____

Please add any other information about your background that you feel is relevant:

_____

_____

_____

_____

_____

_____

_____

_____

_____

_____

_____

_____

_____

_____

_____

_____

_____

_____

_____

_____

_____

_____

_____

_____

_____

_____

_____

_____

_____

_____

_____

Appendix B

Custody/Access Dispute Contract
(Adapted from the Court Clinic in Ottawa, Canada)

The purpose of this contract is to obtain written agreement that the therapist will not be asked to participate in any litigation regarding the custody/access dispute. If the therapist is asked to participate in litigation, the therapist's neutral role with the family may be compromised. This is likely to seriously jeopardize any progress that may have been made in therapy. In order to prevent such deterioration of any therapy, it is crucial that I/we have every reassurance that there will be absolutely no involvement on my/our part in current or future litigation between the parents. This is best accomplished by both parents signing this statement:

We wish to enlist the services of _____ in the treatment of
(name of agency or therapist)

our family. We understand that such treatment will be compromised if information

revealed therein is brought to the attention of the court in the course of a custody/access

dispute. Accordingly, we mutually pledge that we will neither individually nor jointly

involve _____in any litigation whatsoever. We will neither
(name of agency or therapist)

request nor require _____to provide testimony in court. If the
(name of agency or therapist)

services of a mental health professional are desired for court purposes, the services of a

person outside of _____must be enlisted.
(name of agency or therapist)

We have read the above, discussed these provisions with any attorney that we may be involved with at the present time, and agree to proceed with the therapy.

_____   _____
Date   **Signature of parent**

_____   _____
Date   **Signature of parent**

_____   _____
Date   **Witness/(Therapist)**

Appendix C

Sample Letter from the Therapist
for the Client's Last Session

February 5, 2013

Dear Cory,

This scrapbook is a very special book. It has the important activities we did together when you came to see me. Over the years, you can look at this book as a reminder of all that you learned in therapy.

Each time you came here, it was wonderful to greet you with our special handshake. It was fun to learn all about you when we played Balloon Bounce: I learned that you love the color red, you enjoy playing soccer, and you have many special talents like coloring and baking.

When you first came to see me, you had a lot of sad, angry, mixed-up feelings about your parents' divorce. We did many activities to help you talk about your feelings, understand about divorce, and learn ways to feel better. You especially enjoyed when we played Guess Which Hand and Forever Love. And you learned to pop your worries away with bubbles, use Cookie Breathing to calm your body, and do Stomp, Freeeeze, Cookie Breeeethe when you feel angry. You learned so much — way to go!

Cory, I want to tell you how lucky I feel to have known you. You are a super-duper kid! I wish you lots of smiley faces because you deserve to be happy!

Yours truly,

Banana

References and Resources

Amato, P. R. (2010). Research on divorce: Continuing trends and new developments. *Journal of Marriage and Family,* 72, 650–666.

Association of Family and Conciliation Courts. (2010). *Guidelines for court-involved therapy.* Madison, WI: Association of Family and Conciliation Courts.

Bacon, B. L., & McKenzie, B. (2004). Parent education after separation/divorce. *Family Court Review*, 42, 85-98.

Baris, M. A., Coates, C. A., Duvall, B. B., Garrity, C. B., Johnson, E. T., & LaCrosse, R. R. (2000). *Working with high-conflict families of divorce: A guide for professionals.* Lanham, MD: Jason Aronson Publishers.

Barsky, A., & Gould, J. (2002). *Clinicians in court: A guide to subpoenas, depositions, testifying, and everything else you need to know.* New York: Guilford Press.

Blakeslee, S., & Wallerstein, J. S. (2004). *Second chances: Men, women and children a decade after divorce.* New York: Mariner Books.

Carmichael, K. D. (2006). *Play therapy: An introduction.* Uppersaddle River, NJ: Pearson Education.

Cavett, A. (2010). *Structured play-based interventions for engaging children in therapy.* West Conshohocken, PA: Infinity Publishing.

Cummings, E. M., & Davies, P. T. (2010). *Marital conflict and children: An emotional security perspective.* New York: Guilford Press.

Davies, D. (2010). *Child development: A practitioner's guide.* (3rd ed.). New York: Guilford Press.

Emery, R. (2006). *The truth about children and divorce.* New York: Penguin Group.

Favaro, P. (2009). *Smart parenting during and after divorce.* New York: McGraw Hill.

Fidler, B. J., Bala, N., & Saini, M. A. (2013). *Children who resist post-separation parental contact: A differential approach for legal and mental health professionals.* New York: Oxford University Press.

Fidnick, L. S., Koch, K. A., Greenberg, L. R., & Sullivan, M. (2011). Association of family and conciliation courts white paper guidelines for court-involved therapy: A best practice approach for mental health professionals. *Family Court Review*, 49(3), 557-563.

Freeman, R., Abel, D., Cowper-Smith, M., & Stein, L. (2004). Reconnecting children with absent parents: A model for intervention. *Family Court Review*, 42, 439-459.

Garrity, C., & Barris, M. (1994). *Caught in the middle: Protecting the children of high-conflict divorce.* New York: Lexington.

Gil, E. (1994). *Play in family therapy.* New York: Guilford Press.

Giordano, M., Landreth, G., & Jones, L. (2005). *A practical handbook for building the play therapy relationship.* Lanham, MD: Jason Aronson Publishers.

Goodyear-Brown, P. (2005). *Digging for buried treasure: 52 more prop-based play therapy techniques.* Brentwood, TN: Paris Goodyear-Brown.

Goodyear-Brown, P. (2010). *The worry wars: An anxiety workbook for kids and their helpful adults.* Brentwood, TN: Paris Goodyear-Brown.

Grych, J. H. (2005). Interparental conflict as a risk factor for child maladjustment: Implications for the development of prevention programs. *Family Court Review,* 43(1), 97-108.

Johnston, J. R. (2005). Clinical work with parents in entrenched custody disputes. In L. Gunsberg & P. Hymowitz (Eds.), *A handbook of divorce and custody: Forensic, developmental, and clinical perspectives* (pp. 343-364). Hillsdale, NJ: The Analytic Press.

Johnston, J. R., & Roseby, V. (1997). *In the name of the child: A developmental approach to understanding and helping children of high conflict divorce.* New York: The Free Press.

Kelly, J. B. (2002). Psychological and legal interventions for parents and children in custody and access disputes: Current research and practice. *Virginia Journal of Social Policy and the Law,* 10(1), 129-163.

Kelly, J. B., & Emery, R. (2003). Children's adjustment following divorce: Risk & resilience perspectives. *Family Relations,* 52, 352-362.

Kenney-Noziska, S. (2008). *Techniques – techniques – techniques: Play-based activities for children, adolescents, and families.* West Conshohocken, PA: Infinity Publishing.

Landreth, G. (2012). *Play therapy: The art of the relationship* (3rd ed.). Muncie, IN: Accelerated Development Press.

Lansky, V. (2008). 101 ways to tell your child I love you. Deephaven, MN: The Book Peddlers.

Lite, L. (2005). *Indigo ocean dreams: 4 children's stories designed to decrease stress, anger and anxiety while increasing self-esteem and self-awareness* (CD and Storybook). Marietta, GA: Stress Free Kids.

Long, N., & Forehand, R. (2002). *Making divorce easier on your child.* New York: Contemporary Books.

Lowenstein, L. (1999). *Creative interventions for troubled children & youth.* Toronto, ON: Champion Press.

Lowenstein, L. (2002). *More creative interventions for troubled children & youth.* Toronto, ON: Champion Press.

Lowenstein, L. (2006a). *Creative interventions for children of divorce.* Toronto, ON: Champion Press.

Lowenstein, L. (2006b). *Creative interventions for bereaved children.* Toronto, ON: Champion Press.

Lowenstein, L. (Ed.) (2008). *Assessment and treatment activities for children, adolescents, and families: Practitioners share their most effective techniques.* Toronto, ON: Champion Press.

Lowenstein, L. (Ed.) (2010a). *Assessment and treatment activities for children, adolescents, and families Volume Two: Practitioners share their most effective techniques.* Toronto, ON: Champion Press.

Lowenstein, L. (Ed.) (2010b). *Creative family therapy techniques: Play, art, and expressive activities to engage children in family sessions.* Toronto, ON: Champion Press.

Lowenstein, L. (Ed.) (2011). *Assessment and treatment activities for children, adolescents, and families Volume Three: Practitioners share their most effective techniques.* Toronto, ON: Champion Press.

McGuire, D. K., & McGuire, D. E. (2001). *Linking parents to play therapy*. Philadelphia: Brunner-Routledge.

Neuman, G. (1998). *Helping your kids cope with divorce the sandcastles way*. New York: Random House.

Pedro-Carroll, J. (2010). *Putting children first: Proven parenting strategies for helping children thrive through divorce*. New York: Avery/Penguin.

Pedro-Carroll, J. L., & Jones, S. H. (2005). A preventive play intervention to foster children's resilience in the aftermath of divorce. In L. A. Reddy, T. M. Files-Hall, & C. E. Schaefer (Eds.), *Empirically based play interventions for children* (pp. 51-75). Washington, DC: American Psychological Association.

Schaefer, C. E. (Ed). (2003). *Foundations of play therapy*. New Jersey: John Wiley & Sons.

Schaefer, C. E., & Reid, S. (Eds). (2001). *Game play: Therapeutic use of childhood Games*. (2nd ed.). New York: John Wiley & Sons.

Schneider, M. F., & Zuckerberg, J. (1996). *Difficult questions kids ask (and are afraid to ask) about divorce*. New York: Fireside.

Shirk, S. R., & Karver, M. (2003). Prediction of treatment outcome from relationship variables in child and adolescent therapy. *Journal of Consulting and Clinical Psychology*, 71(3), 452–464.

Teyber, E. (2001). *Helping children cope with divorce*. New York: John Wiley & Sons.

Wallerstein, J. S. (1983). Children of divorce: The psychological tasks of the child. *American Journal of Orthopsychiatry* 53, 230-243.

Warshak, R. A. (2010). *Divorce poison: How to protect your family from badmouthing and brainwashing*. New York: Harper.

Suppliers of Therapy Materials

Anna's Toy Depot (People figurines, doll houses, therapy materials)
www.annastoydepot.com

Child Therapy Toys (People figurines, doll houses, therapy materials)
www.childtherapytoys.com
***Get 15% off when you cite code: Lowenstein

Self Esteem Shop (People figurines, doll houses, therapy materials)
www.selfesteemshop.com

Toys of the Trade (Miniature figurines)
www.toysofthetrade.com

Oriental Trading Company (Prizes, novelty items)
www.orientaltrading.com

Organizations and Web Sites

Canadian Association for Child and Play Therapy
www.cacpt.com

Association for Play Therapy
www.a4pt.org

British Association of Play Therapists
www.bapt.info

International Society for Child and Play Therapy
www.playtherapy.org

Play Therapy Australia
www.playtherapyaustralia.com

Association of Family and Conciliation Courts
www.afccnet.org

Kids' Turn
www.kidsturn.org/kt

UpToParents
www.UpToParents.org

Also by Liana Lowenstein

Creative Interventions for Troubled Children and Youth

More Creative Interventions for Troubled Children & Youth

Creative Interventions for Bereaved Children

Creative Interventions for Children of Divorce

Assessment and Treatment Techniques for Children, Adolescents, and Families: Practitioners Share Their Most Effective Techniques (Volumes One through Three)

Creative Family Therapy Techniques: Play, Art, and Expressive Therapies to Engage Children in Family Sessions

Cory Helps Kids Cope with Sexual Abuse: Playful Activities for Traumatized Children

***For further information about the above books and upcoming publications, go to www.lianalowenstein.com